MYplace

FOR BIBLE STUDY

Published by First Place for Health
Galveston, Texas, USA
www.firstplaceforhealth.com
Printed in the USA

ISBN: 978-1-942425-46-5

CONTENTS

MY PLACE FOR BIBLE STUDY

Breaking Through

FOREWORD

I was introduced to First Place for Health in 1993 by my mother-in-law, who had great concern for the welfare of her grandchildren. I was overweight and overwrought! God used that first Bible study to start me on my journey to health, wellness, and a life of balance.

Our desire at First Place for Health is for you to begin that same journey. We want you to experience the freedom that comes from an intimate relationship with Jesus Christ and witness His love for you through reading your Bible and through prayer. To this end, we have designed each day's study (which will take about fifteen to twenty minutes to complete) to help you discover the deep truths of the Bible. Also included is a weekly Bible memory verse to help you hide God's Word in your heart. As you start focusing on these truths, God will begin a great work in you.

At the beginning of Jesus' ministry, when He was teaching from the book of Isaiah, He said to the people, "The Spirit of the Lord is on me, because he has anointed me to preach good news to the poor. He has sent me to proclaim freedom for the prisoners and recovery of sight for the blind, to release the oppressed, to proclaim the year of the Lord's favor" (Luke 4:18–19). Jesus came to set us free—whether that is from the chains of compulsivity, addiction, gluttony, overeating, under eating, or just plain unbelief. It is our prayer that He will bring freedom to your heart so you may experience abundant life.

God bless you as you begin this journey toward a life of liberty.

Vicki Heath, First Place for Health National Director

ABOUT THE AUTHOR

Janet Holm McHenry is a national speaker and award-winning author of twenty-five books, including two other First Place for Health Bible studies, *Training for Success* and *Stronger Every Day*. Her Christian living books include six related to prayer, including the best-selling *PrayerWalk* and her newest, *The Complete Guide to the Prayers of Jesus*. Janet's prayerwalking practices have been featured in Health magazine, First for Women, Woman's Day, and many other publications, and she speaks frequently on radio programs and podcasts about prayer, prayerwalking, personal and spiritual disciplines, and her Personal Trainer, Jesus.

A FP4H group leader, Janet has enjoyed speaking at First Place for Health wellness workshops, prayerwalking events, prayer conferences, and retreats. She directs the prayer ministries at The Bridge Church in Reno, is Sierra County coordinator and on the state leadership team for the National Day of Prayer, and created the online course called Prayer School. Janet also leads the large internet through-the-Bible-in-a-year group called Bible Girls and loves digging into God's Word.

A former high school English teacher and academic advisor, Janet and her husband, Craig, have raised four adult children in the Sierra Valley in northeast California, where he is a rancher and where she continues to prayerwalk on behalf of her community. Janet is a life coach and the host of the Sierra Valley Writers Retreat. More information about her ministry—Looking Up!—and her writings can be accessed through her website, www.janetmchenry.com.

ABOUT THE CONTRIBUTOR

Lisa Lewis, who provided the menus and recipes in this study, is the author of *Healthy Happy Cooking*. Lisa's cooking skills have been a part of First Place for Health wellness weeks and other events for many years. She provided recipes for seventeen of the First Place for Health Bible studies and is a contributing author in *Better Together* and *Healthy Holiday Living*. She partners with community networks, including the Real Food Project, to bring healthy cooking classes to underserved areas. She is dedicated to bringing people together around the dinner table with healthy, delicious meals that are easy to prepare. Lisa lives in Galveston and is married to John. They have three children: Tal, Hunter, and Harper. Visit www.healthyhappycook.com for more delicious inspiration.

INTRODUCTION

First Place for Health is a Christ-centered health program that emphasizes balance in the physical, mental, emotional, and spiritual areas of life. The First Place for Health program is meant to be a daily process. As we learn to keep Christ first in our lives, we will find that He is the One who satisfies our hunger and our every need.

This Bible study is designed to be used in conjunction with the First Place for Health program but can be beneficial for anyone interested in obtaining a balanced lifestyle. The Bible study has been created in a seven-day format, with the last two days reserved for reflection on the material studied. Keep in mind that the ultimate goal of studying the Bible is not only for knowledge but also for application and a changed life. Don't feel anxious if you can't seem to find the correct answer. Many times, the Word will speak differently to different people, depending on where they are in their walk with God and the season of life they are experiencing. Be prepared to discuss with your fellow First Place for Health members what you learned that week through your study.

There are some additional components included with this study that will be helpful as you pursue the goal of giving Christ first place in every area of your life:

- **Leader Discussion Guide:** This discussion guide is provided to help the First Place for Health leader guide a group through this Bible study. It includes ideas for facilitating a First Place for Health class discussion for each week of the Bible study.

- **Jump Start Recipes:** There are seven days of recipes--breakfast, lunch and dinner-- to get you started.

- **Steps for Spiritual Growth:** This section will provide you with some basic tips for how to memorize Scripture and make it a part of your life, establish a quiet time with God each day, and share your faith with others..

- **First Place for Health Member Survey:** Fill this out and bring it to your first meeting. This information will help your leader know your interests and talents.

- **Personal Weight and Measurement Record:** Use this form to keep a record of your weight loss. Record any loss or gain on the chart after the weigh-in at each week's meeting.

- **Weekly Prayer Partner Forms:** Fill out this form before class and place it into a basket during the class meeting. After class, you will draw out a prayer request form, and this will be your prayer partner for the week. Try to call or email the person sometime before the next class meeting to encourage that person.

- **100-Mile Club:** A worthy goal we encourage is for you to complete 100 miles of exercise during your twelve weeks in First Place for Health. There are many activities listed on pages 265-266 that count toward your goal of 100 miles and a handy tracker to track your miles.

- **Live It Trackers:** Your Live It Tracker is to be completed at home and turned in to your leader at your weekly First Place for Health meeting. The Tracker is designed to help you practice mindfulness and stay accountable with regard to your eating and exercise habits.

WEEK ONE: FROM BONDAGE TO BREAKTHROUGH

SCRIPTURE MEMORY VERSE
And when they heard that the Lord was concerned about them and had seen their misery, they bowed down and worshiped. Exodus 4:31

Each of us is on a health journey. For some of us that journey is helping us feel stronger and better equipped for God's calling on our lives. However, others of us are on a downward spiral. Personally, I know that my struggles to keep off weight in my past led to several surgeries, joint pain, and a wrestling with blood sugar and cholesterol numbers. However, I am now determined to be my best, so that I can live the next years free from self-sabotaged behaviors that create health issues and stress. Living our best life health-wise means that we may have to break through from that which would weigh us down to a confident, productive lifestyle serving God.

During this study we will go on a journey from bondage to brokenness to breakthrough, following the stories of the Israelites as they leave slavery in Egypt, wander in the desert, and then finally head into the Promised Land. Perhaps we can identify some with their stories. In Egypt they were overworked and unable to live and worship as people of God. In fact, they had gotten so used to physical hardships, they had forgotten what it was like to be free. And even when freed from literal slavery, they still wanted to go back to the land that had kept them in bondage.

If you've been on a weight and health yo-yo pattern, you might sympathize with their mistaken perceptions about their condition. But perhaps you are now ready to break away from the past into a daily practice of making your physical, mental, emotional, and spiritual health a priority. It takes courage to step away from past habits, thinking, and attitudes into a promised land of health. But together, we can do just that.

—— DAY 1: FACING THE TRUTH
Father God, I see that my health journey can be headed either toward You or away from You. Help me head in Your direction. Amen.

Each of us has something holding us back from living an unencumbered life so that we can follow God's leading fully. That might be a combo of worry, anxiety, and fear or a tendency to give in to temptation or even depression. The first step in breaking through and away from any of those struggles is to face the truth. Years ago when my knee gave way going down stairs, I had to recognize that my weight had gotten out of control. When I began the practice of prayerwalking, I also found that irrational fears and depression also had strongholds on me.

As I walked in one particular dark area each day, I sensed great fear gripping me. It was rather irrational, really, as I was only a block from home. Somehow I knew the enemy wanted me to quit praying for my community, so instead of running home, I began speaking my prayers aloud and asking God to break the oppression and give me strength. One day as I approached that area, I realized that fear no longer had a grip on me—there or elsewhere. Sometimes we are so immersed in our pain or our fear that it oddly becomes our new reality—and even a strange comfort zone.

This was true for the Israelites. While they had lived freely during the time of Joseph, later generations found themselves enslaved under a cruel pharaoh unlike the welcoming one who elevated Joseph to second in command. We learn from Exodus 1 that the new king oppressed the Hebrews with cruel labor practices and even ordered infanticide to weaken and kill off their population. Eventually, though, God raised up one of those male Hebrew babies through miraculous intervention and then called Moses to lead the Israelites out of Egypt.

Read Exodus 6:1-9. What did the Lord instruct Moses to say to the Israelites?

_____
_____
_____

How did the Israelites respond to Moses (v. 9)? What caused this response?

_____
_____
_____

Read Exodus 6:10-12. How did the Israelites' response discourage Moses?

_____
_____
_____

What truths had Moses and the Israelites forgotten (review vv. 1-8)?

_____

_____

_____

What role can discouragement play in our thinking when we are facing a personal struggle such as fear or temptation?

_____

_____

_____

We all may have struggles caused by external situations over which we may have no control: job loss, an illness, a marriage partner's infidelity. When those difficulties arise, they can prompt negative mental and emotional responses in us that can send us into a downward slide. Complete the following sentence, identifying the greatest internal personal struggle you may be facing today (worry, fear, anxiety, temptation, self-sabotage, self-loathing, lack of faith, etc.).

Today I acknowledge that I am wrestling with the following internal issue:

_____

_____

_____

But take heart! As Tony Evans has said, "Brokenness is often the road to break-through. Be encouraged." You can break out of whatever is holding you back, and taking part in this First Place for Health study can guide you to a Promised Land place.

_____

_____

_____

Lord God, today I admit I am wrestling with an internal issue that ultimately reflects my lack of trust in You. I give that freely to You now and ask for Your help. Amen.

—— DAY 2: WEIGHING A DECISION

Father God, now that I have given my struggle to You, I am also making the decision to leave it behind. I choose this day to move forward. Amen.

Even while we recognize that we are struggling with something such as fear of failure, we may tend to shift blame to someone else or the external situation in our lives. For example, for years I gave up on losing weight because I had failed so many times. My thought was, *Why try if I know I'll fail anyway?* Moses struggled with doubts and fears too. The Lord called him to lead the people out of Egypt back to Canaan. However, Moses had two fears—that Pharaoh would not listen to him, but also that the Israelites themselves would not follow him. As a result, Moses created several seemingly rational and human reasons to try to get out of God's call on his life.

Read Exodus 3:7-9. Who saw the suffering of God's people? What did He determine to do?

_____

_____

_____

Now read Exodus 3:10. What two tasks did God give Moses?

_____

_____

Complete the following chart, explaining (1) Moses's various responses to God's call on his life and (2) God's responses to those objections.

SCRIPTURE	MOSES'S OBJECTION	GOD'S RESPONSE
Exodus 3:11-12		
Exodus 3:13-15		
Exodus 4:1-8		
Exodus 4:10-12		
Exodus 4:13-16		

When we know we are supposed to follow God's leading and make changes in our lives, it's easy to come up with a long list of excuses not to do just that. Those reasons might have very good human logic, but they often discount God's goodness, his purpose for our lives, and his power. What reasons or excuses have you had for not moving forward in a more positive way in your life?

_____

_____

_____

It's satisfying to have a scapegoat for my own struggles, but I know I'm responsible for my body's health. President Theodore Roosevelt once said, "If you could kick the person in the pants responsible for most of your trouble, you wouldn't sit for a month." Acknowledging those excuses is another good step toward living a healthier life. Now give them to God as you say this prayer.

Lord God, I am tired of making excuses for not making progress in this area of my life. I acknowledge that in doing so I have not trusted in Your Spirit's power to change me and have not fully lived out Your purpose for me. I now leave them behind. Amen.

—— DAY 3: TAKING FIRST STEPS
Lord, help me make the first steps in my wellness journey. Give me the courage to step away and do the right thing. Amen.

Once God convinced Moses to lead the Hebrews out of Egypt, Moses then had to approach Pharaoh for permission to do just that. Do you remember from yesterday's study that it was the Lord God himself who said he would rescue the people and lead them to the land of milk and honey? Moses was the earthly appointee to carry out God's plan. God gave Moses the words to say each of those dozen times he confronted Pharaoh to plead for the Hebrews' release (Exodus 5-11). Even though the scripture says Moses continued to object to the Lord, he overcame his fears and did what God asked him to do. In other words, Moses overcame those fears through action. And it's probable that the miracles and the ten plagues not only convinced Pharaoh of God's power, but also convinced Moses himself and the watching Israelites.

Read Exodus 4:18-30. What first step did Moses take (v. 18)? Why do you think he did this?

_____

_____

_____

What reassurance did God give Moses and what second step did Moses take (vv. 19-20)?

_____

_____

_____

In verses 21-23 the Lord continues a dialogue with Moses, coaching him on his journey from Midian back to Egypt about what he might expect. We may be surprised to read the Lord "was about to kill him" (v. 24), but Moses had failed to dedicate his son to the Lord by circumcising him, so Zipporah—clearly understanding the seriousness of Moses's omission—did that task herself.

Whom did God send to meet Moses (vv. 27-28)? Why do you think the Lord sent him?

_____

_____

_____

What four actions did Moses and Aaron do prior to meeting with Pharaoh for the first time (vv. 29-30)?

_____

_____

_____

What might your first steps be to begin your breakthrough journey? When will you do this?

_____

_____

_____

Lord God, I know I can confidently take transformative steps in my life because I know You will coach me, provide counselors around me, and be with me. Amen.

—— DAY 4: FOLLOWING THROUGH

Father, I have taken the first steps toward wellness. Help me continue to be faithful, trusting You all the way. Amen.

It took a lot of signs and wonders for Pharaoh to understand that the Lord of the universe was behind Moses's request to release the Hebrews. Those included a staff turning into a snake as well as plagues of blood, frogs, gnats, flies, livestock deaths, boils, hail, locusts, darkness, and the deaths of firstborn sons and livestock. Other than the final plague, the Hebrew people experienced these plagues as well. The plague of frogs provides an interesting commentary on us and how we can often hang on to our misery instead of following through with decisions that we make.

Read Exodus 8:1-15. What does Pharaoh tell Moses to do (v. 8)?

_____

_____

_____

Then when Moses asks Pharaoh when he would want to get rid of the frogs, what does Pharaoh say (v. 10)?

_____

_____

_____

Pharaoh's answer may sound familiar. I have lived decades of that same response: "tomorrow." When will I start a healthier eating plan? Tomorrow. When will I add strengthening exercises to my exercise routine? Tomorrow. When will I begin a new work project? Tomorrow. In the interim, time is ticking away...and I'm spending yet another day not choosing the best for myself. We often choose to live with a frog-like plague instead of choosing God's abundance for ourselves.

Putting off healthy choices may have to do with a person's tendency toward perfectionism. Some of us don't take on new challenges unless we feel we can do them perfectly. Check off which of the following is helpful for you:

- ○ Decide something does not have to be done perfectly to be tried.
- ○ Start small. If, for example, you're hooked on sweets, have one small something a day and be sure to put it down on your Live It Tracker.

- O Write down your daily, weekly, and monthly tasks on a to-do list calendar so as to plan when you will complete each one.
- O Simplify your life by clearing your schedule and home of the things you know bog you down so that you can focus on that which is important.
- O Instead of overthinking each tasks set before you, just start the first one.
- O Refuse to give in to distractions, such as online social media, television, and even music.
- O Schedule your fun activities for a time after your task is completed. Use them as a reward.[1]

What kind of follow-through do you need to take in your wellness journey? Instead of waiting until tomorrow or the next week or the next, what will you do today that demonstrates your resolution to follow through?

_____

_____

_____

Father, I know you have been patient with me over the years...despite my failures to follow through with new health and other resolutions. Give me the strength to immediately step into better patterns for my life. Amen.

——— DAY 5: BREAKING THROUGH

Lord God, I know there will continue to be external challenges ahead, but because You are with me, I know we can break through them as well. Amen.

Change is hard, whether we are starting a new job, moving to a different city, or simply changing our health routines. Can you imagine moving a mountain of people, as Moses did? The Exodus was a pivotal, historic event. Numbers 1:46 tells us that 603,550 men were counted in a census of men able to serve in Israel's army, meaning at least two million people had escaped Egypt under Moses's command. Again, can you imagine moving an entire city the size of Houston or Chicago? That's a lot of change for a multitude of lives. And often change does not come easily.

The word *exodus* comes from the Greek *exodos*, which means "a going out, a journeying forth, a departure"; broken down, *exodus* means "out" and "way." When we determine to make a change, we are moving out of something former into a new way. We are leaving the past behind—breaking out of old ways of thinking and behavior—to embrace new possibilities. For the Israelites that meant leaving captivity and oppression. For us who struggle with addictive food and other negative behaviors, exodus can also mean leaving a negative past and shifting into a healthier lifestyle.

Read Exodus 12:24-51. As God directed him, Moses told the Hebrews to indicate that they were the Lord's people by painting their exterior doorframes with the blood of a lamb—called the Passover lamb. The blood was a public declaration of their faith in God, and God honored that faith by then passing over those homes in the final plague of the death of the firstborn.

What instructions did Moses give the people in verses 24-27?

_____

_____

_____

How did the people respond (verses 27-28)?

_____

_____

_____

Why was it important that the people do exactly as the Lord (through Moses) instructed?

_____

_____

_____

Sometimes we need a not-so-pleasant impetus for us to change. For those of us needing health improvement, that might mean aching joints. For the Hebrews in the Exodus story, the impetus was a directive in Exodus 12:31-32 from Pharaoh: "Up! Leave my people, you and the Israelites! Go, worship the Lord as you have requested. Take your flocks and herds, as you have said, and go. And also bless me." The people had no choice now: the king and other Egyptians were ushering them out.

Read Exodus 12:34-42. How did the people respond?

_____

_____

_____

What other details about the Israelites' exodus did you notice in the text?

_____

_____

The Israelites left in a hurry. There was no time to wait for bread to rise. They picked up what essentials they would need and left the rest behind. First Place for Health national director emeritus Carole Lewis has often said, "Do the next right thing." Sometimes we complicate change. We create checklists and make pros and cons charts before making a decision to bring about change in our lives, when we simply should just do the next right thing: leave the destructive behavior and start the new, better one.

What would help you start a better path toward wellness?

_____

_____

_____

Lord God, help me not overthink the changes I want to make in my life but simply do what you would have me do. Amen.

—— DAY 6: REFLECTION AND APPLICATION

Lord, you are the chains breaker. Help me break free of that which is keeping me from freedom. Amen.

As a college freshman, Jeanne Donovan chose a career in law enforcement. While she had to exercise and lose enough weight for the California Highway Patrol to hire her, she finally made it and survived the rigorous boot camp. However, this did not last long. In the next five years she did a complete turnaround, and her career ended after three car accidents, a pursuit, a shooting, a fight, and two back surgeries. In the midst of all of that, Jeanne met her husband, became "Mom" to his son and daughter, and gave birth to two more daughters. "I dearly loved my family," Jeanne said, "but I was fat, miserable, and depressed."

Over the next twenty years and numerous weight loss programs, she kept losing and gaining the same twenty pounds. Health issues, along with chronic back pain, slowed her progress. Then in 2007 Jeanne found a First Place for Health Bible study and Carole Lewis's book *Divine Diet*. "From the moment I began reading," Jeanne said,

"I knew this was what I needed." She did the study by herself for several years, lost thirty-six pounds, and then started a First Place group at her church. Now a FP4H networking leader, Jeanne said her walk with the Lord through First Place has "healed many of my wounds as well and has made my family and me so much healthier."

Jeanne Donovan's first step toward wellness was to do a First Place for Health Bible study. You have made that choice as well. What specific breakthrough goals in the following areas will you set for the next two months as you work through this Bible study?

Physical

_____

_____

_____

Mental

_____

_____

_____

Emotional

_____

_____

_____

Spiritual

_____

_____

_____

Lord God, I give myself to you during this study. Make me aware of healthy changes I can make in the coming days and weeks. May I be more like you each and every day. Amen.

—— DAY 7: REFLECTION AND APPLICATION

Lord God, I have made the decision to make changes in my life that will be good for my physical, mental, emotional, and spiritual health. Help me be good for my word.

Television's Phil McGraw, a clinical psychologist known as Dr. Phil, often asks those who seek his counsel, "How's that working for you?" Like the Israelites, who worked for generations in slavery, we can get used to our misery. We want to change, but change cannot happen magically. It requires reflective thinking, motivation, and different behaviors to put into place.

Some of the questions we can ask ourselves include the following:

1. What is true about your situation of concern?

2. What is true about what you *cannot* do to change your situation?

3. What is true about what you *can* do?

4. To what extent have you trusted God about your situation?

5. How might you embrace the possibilities of change?

6. To what extent are your pursuing your own health, to include getting enough sleep, eating nutritious foods, drinking enough water, avoiding caffeine and alcohol, pursuing exercise, and getting regular medical checkups? How might you change those practices?

7. How could you renew your mind to get rid of negative input that you feed yourself, to include self-talk and nonproductive media?

8. What spiritual life practices are you pursuing, to include reading your Bible, praying, and fellowshipping with others of the faith?

Write out the scripture memory verse for Week One:

This memory verse indicates that when the people understood that God was concerned and saw their misery, they responded by bowing down and worshipping Him.

Write a short prayer of dedication that indicates your earnestness to follow God's leading into your Promised Land ahead.

Father, I kneel before you now and ask for your continued, patient mercies toward me. I see where I am today and how You might lead me. Take me there, Lord God. Amen.

[1] Janet Holm McHenry, *50 Life Lessons for Grads* (Franklin TN: Worthy Inspired/ Hachette, 2018), 126.

WEEK TWO: FROM CHALLENGE TO GOD'S CONTROL

SCRIPTURE MEMORY VERSE
Moses answered the people, "Do not be afraid. Stand firm and you will see the deliverance the Lord will bring you today." Exodus 14:13

During my semester sabbatical from teaching, I had planned to write a book, not navigate two surgeries. While I had never taken time off from work in the past, this project was going to require a tremendous amount of work, so my school district approved the leave. Shortly into that season, I learned our younger son would need major knee surgery. After his hospital recovery, the surgeon showed me how to set up the heavy movement machine and ice machine for the therapy he would need at home.

The doctor's last words were, "Be careful lifting these heavy machines, or you'll find yourself needing back surgery."

I followed all the doctor's advice, except that last statement—often moving the machines from room to room when my son wanted a change of scenery. After weeks of that, I began experiencing level 10 back pain and after three weeks flat in bed, a neurosurgeon told me, "You have the worst herniated disc I've ever seen."

After surgery I rebounded quickly, but those months of caregiving and recuperating certainly detoured me from my plans.

—— DAY 1: FACING A DETOUR
Lord God, help me understand how the detours of life can work for my benefit.

Life can provide all kinds of detours for us. Sometimes our health derails our plans. Or losing a job can provide financial difficulties. In those circumstances we can feel completely out of control. However, none of this surprises God, whose hands have filtered these diversions.

The Israelites experienced detours and challenges after leaving Egypt. While it would seem logical to travel directly from Point A (Egypt) to Point B (the Promised Land) as the shortest possible route, God had other plans.

What circumstances in your life seemingly sent you on a detour? How did that work out?

Read Exodus 13:17-22. Why did God not lead the Israelites through the Philistine country (see v. 17)?

In which direction did they travel instead (v. 18)? And how were they prepared?

The scriptures do not indicate how the Israelites reacted emotionally to God's detour from a straight path to one that would head toward the Red Sea and eventually into desert wanderings. But what did they do, and how did they know where to go (vv. 21-22)?

Explain how the Lord guided them.

When we face events that seemingly are taking our lives onto a bumpy side road, we are challenged to make two mental shifts—to accept the situation and then to adapt to it. When something is out of our hands, a healthy posture would be to give ourselves permission to stop worrying. Worry won't change our circumstances and may actually create negative health symptoms. Instead, we can give God our life's steering wheel by remembering His care for us in the past so that we change mental gears from anxiety and fear to trust in God for the present situation as well as the days ahead. When our mind has moved from fear to faith, then we can focus on the smaller details we can control, such as healthy eating and the words that we speak in response to our situation. Just as God guided the Exodus masses to the right path, he will guide us as well.

Perhaps something difficult has occurred in your life recently, so that you're waiting for life to change. How can you know that God will lead you from day to day, just as he led the Israelites?

Father, life does seem out of control lately, with all kinds of uncertainties. Please provide clarity and guide my steps.

—— DAY 2: FACING FEAR
Lord, help me face my fears and move forward, trusting You for each step of the way.

Detours often digress into full-blown hardships. A physical symptom might lead to doctors' appointments and then a tough diagnosis. A tough argument with a teenaged child might develop into a season of rebellion. A cutback at work might precede a layoff. We all experience such seasons in our lives when we feel as though we are up against an immovable wall with seemingly little hope for resolution.

What recent set of circumstances has thrown you for a loop?

The Israelites also faced what they thought was an immovable wall of sorts—the Red Sea. In Chapter 14 in Exodus we learn that the Lord directed Moses to take the Israelites from Migdol (thought to be the northernmost city in Egypt) to an area toward the Red Sea. Scripture tells us that this surprising move would make Pharaoh change his mind about letting the Hebrew slaves go to pursue them (Exodus 14:4).

Read Exodus 14:4. How would God gain glory? For what purpose did God plan such a strategy?

When we are mired in our own struggles, it is easy to lose sight of the fact that God could work through those who are giving us grief for the purpose of displaying Himself to them.

Read Exodus 14:5-31. What was the Israelites' first reaction when Pharoah's mighty forces approached (vv. 11-12)?

_____
_____
_____
_____

How did Moses respond to the people (vv. 13-14)?

_____
_____
_____

Moses told the people to not be afraid but to stand still. What do you think that instruction meant?

_____
_____
_____
_____

Moses also told the people the Lord would fight for them...and to just stay calm. If they had not taken his counsel, what might have ensued?

_____
_____
_____
_____

Sometimes we must step out and take action; at other times we have to be still and stay calm. In stressful times what specific behaviors could we employ that would be good for our health:
Physical health: _____
Mental health: _____
Emotional health: _____
Spiritual health: _____

Lord, you are faithful. When I stand still and stay calm, I will be in the best position to allow You to navigate me through life's turmoil.

—— DAY 3: STEPPING THROUGH
Lord, be with me as I step through this challenge.

With the Egyptian army breathing down the necks of the Israelites, Moses told the people to be still and stay calm, because the Lord would fight the battle ahead. While those words might make Moses appear to be faith-filled and confident about what God would do, there seem to be some missing lines in scripture.

Read Exodus 14:15-31. From verse 15 what can we assume about how Moses was feeling?

Then specifically, what actions did the Lord tell Moses to take (vv. 15-16)?

Moses had one job to do: raise his staff and stretch out his hand over the sea. The people had one job to do: "move on" (14:15). The Lord did not tell Moses to fight the Egyptians. The fight was left in God's hands. The people simply had to move forward because God would orchestrate the battle.

And here's what God did. First, the angel of God changed positions—from a place in front of the Israelites to a place behind them to be a protective buffer—and the protective pillar of cloud did the same (v. 19). This cloud brought darkness to the Egyptians but light for the on-the-move Israelites. That was just the setup for the bigger miracle.

Complete the following chart by noting the remaining chronology of events.

REFERENCE	WHAT HAPPENED
Ex. 14:21	
Ex. 14:22	
Ex. 14:23	
Ex. 14:24	
Ex. 14:25	
Ex. 14:26	
Ex. 14:27-28	

What are some principles we learn about facing our fears from this chapter?

_____

_____

_____

How did God get you through a time when you were afraid?

_____

_____

_____

Lord, I know that fears only increase when I do not confront them. Help me face my fears, trust You to help me deal with them, and then move on in Your power and grace.

—— DAY 4: CELEBRATING THE WINS
Lord, sometimes I zone out and get confused during a crisis. Keep me calm and focused so that I clearly know what You would have me do.

From the psalms and other poetry of the Bible, we know that music was important to the Hebrew people, as it has been for Christians throughout the ages. It can see us through trials and is a central part of celebration.

The Israelites had much to celebrate. They escaped their life of slavery under a cruel pharaoh. They crossed through the Red Sea after God parted the waters and made the seabed dry. They watched as the Lord released the waters back into place, drowning the Egyptian army. While their journey ahead would not be easy, they were finally free and ready to celebrate.

Read Exodus 15:1-21. Using the following chart, write a summary of the major points of the poem.

STANZA/VERSES	WHAT IS THE CENTRAL IDEA?
Stanza 1: verses 1-5	
Stanza 2: verses 6-8	
Stanza 3: verses 9-10	
Stanza 4: verses 11-12	
Stanza 5: verses 13-18	

These central ideas or teaching points can model for us how we can respond when facing fear. Even if we are still in the middle of a struggle, we still can remember the Lord's great works, his faithfulness, and times of victory in our lives. Celebrating small victories ("My son called today!" "I lost another pound!" "I made it through my first chemo treatment!") is important too.

Recall a time when you journeyed through a tough, perhaps even fearful season. What were some of the things you learned about yourself, about people, about life in general, and/or about God from that time?

1. _____

2. _____

3. _____

4. _____

Practicing praise and thankfulness changes our brains. Scientists say that expressing gratitude activates the hypothalamus, which is at the base of our brain and regulates hormones responsible for many critical functions, such as body temperature, emotional responses, and survival functions, like appetite and sleep. When gratitude is expressed, dopamine, a pleasure hormone, is released.[1] In other words, celebrating and being thankful for what we do have and what God has done can make us healthier mentally and emotionally and give us a greater perspective of His presence in our lives.

Now turn those lessons into a prayer of thanksgiving and celebration, and share this with your First Place for Health group.

_____

_____

_____

Father, I give you thanks and lift great praise to You for Your faithful hand on my life. I see how You have remained by my side and allowed purpose to rise from my pain.

—— DAY 5: RELYING ON GOD

I want to rely fully on You, Lord. Help me remember You and Your strength and power instead of dwelling on the day-to-day difficulties.

The Hebrews' celebration was short lived. The Israelites' songs quickly turned to complaints when they could not find water in the desert of Shur.

Isn't that true for us too? Even after watching God supply my family's needs year after year, I still fell into grumbles and worries when an appliance broke down or the car would die. My problem was nearsightedness. I only saw what was in my bank account, forgetting that God's resources are without limit. Let's learn from others' misperceptions and mistakes.

Read Exodus 15:22-27. What was the Israelites' problem (vv. 22-23)?

_____

_____

_____

How did the people react (v. 24)?

_____

_____

_____

Notice the progression of action in Exodus 15:25 and complete the chart:

How did Moses respond to the people?	
How did the Lord respond?	
What did Moses then do?	
What were the results?	

When a problem arises, prayer should be our first response, not our last resort. With prayer we go directly to the Problem Solver, Who knows exactly what to do. He then will guide us to wait or take action. In the process His Spirit will settle calm over us, even when the tough situation itself has not resolved.

What was the two-part promise God gave Moses in Exodus 15:26?

_____

_____

_____

What did the Israelites find at their next stopping point (v. 27)?

_____

_____

_____

We will all have desert places in our life's journey. But we will also have seasons of oasis with refreshing springs of nourishment and joy and shade from the harsh desert heat. To what will you cling in those desert and even fearful times? What will sustain you in the hard seasons? Specifically, what will you do to keep yourself from drying out mentally, emotionally, and spiritually until you reach that next oasis?

Father, I thank you for those desert times of my life, because I can now see their purpose in shaping me and drawing me closer to you. May I be mindful to turn to you in prayer as a first response, rather than a last resort.

——— DAY 6: REFLECTION AND APPLICATION
Lord, help me make good choices and stay on track health-wise during times of stress, so that I do not create even greater problems for myself down the road.

After struggling through infertility following the birth of her first child, Amy Gray became pregnant with twins through in-vitro fertilization. She spent eight weeks on bed rest, praying and enjoying quiet time "like I had never experienced before." But at four weeks, she and her husband learned that one of the sacs was empty, and then at eight weeks, the news got even worse. "I lost my only remaining baby," she said, "and was left with nothing."[2]

Amy fell into deep clinical depression. For four more weeks she refused to get out of bed, accept visitors, or return phone calls. "My husband didn't understand or know how to handle me," Amy said. "I was all alone because I felt that even God had abandoned me. I was at rock bottom. Why would God do this to me? I was faithful to the Lord and trusted in Him throughout my infertility experience. I was mad and resentful that He had let me down when I thought my faith was at its strongest."

When she started to re-enter society, she began stuffing her emotions—something she had learned in childhood. "I was so mad at my body that I punished it with excessive amounts of food and drinks"; she buried the pain in food. Already heavy, her overeating only made her problems worse, and she avoided going out in public—to the point of not letting her four-year-old go outside to play so Amy could avoid running into a neighbor. "I'd gone from a happy, energetic woman to a fat and miserable human being."

One of her oldest friends reminded her of Isaiah 61:3: "To all those who grieve, and look to Him, He provides a crown of beauty instead of ashes, an oil of gladness instead of mourning and a garment of praise instead of a spirit of despair and they will be called oaks of righteousness, a planting of the Lord for the display of his splendor." Then Amy learned of First Place for Health and thought, I've tried everything else, what do I have to lose (except weight!) by giving this program a shot, too?

At that point she weighed 226 pounds, the same as the day she had given birth four-and-a-half years earlier. On that first meeting night, it all started to make sense. Amy realized she had asked for God's help and grace in other areas of my life—throughout her fertility issues, in her struggling marriage, with her uncertain career—but she had never thought to call out to Him to help solve her weight problems. She started the First Place program strongly, worked the food plan, sat with the Lord in quiet time, and sought His word through Bible study and scripture memory. She also shouted out in desperation when she was tempted and encouraged others to do the same.

Amy lost 85 pounds through First Place for Health, now runs regularly, and has completed numerous running events. Despite additional financial and other struggles, she writes, "God has remained faithful to me through it and has showed me that, through Him, I can be confident in what maintenance looks and feels like, even during the worst of times!"

Re-examine the physical, mental, emotional, and spiritual goals you set on Day 6 in Week One. What one of those is still problematic for you? What specific plan will you take this coming week to see progress? That may mean making an adjustment to your schedule, changing a negative habit, committing to exercise, or facing a stronghold. Take that matter to prayer as a first response, rather than a last resort.

_____

_____

_____

It is perfectly all right to invest in yourself. Others count on you, and if you are not healthy, you won't be at your best to help them and to do all God has purposed for your life. This can include the following:

- Eating whole, fresh foods.
- Finding an exercise that is not a chore—and doing some of that every day.
- Shutting down electronics early in the evening and getting good sleep.
- Practicing relaxation with a few, restful, quiet moments during the day to pray, meditate, and ask God for His direction.

- Expressing gratitude to God and others.
- Do that which feeds your soul and makes you feel refreshed. This will differ for various people and could include visiting an art museum, taking a hike, asking friends over for dinner, reading a book, cooking or baking, creating art, playing and/or singing music, writing poetry, having lunch with a friend, or even doing gardening or yard work.

Certainly, "doing what is right" in God's sight (Exodus 15:26) includes taking care of your body, feeding your mind with godly instruction, guarding your heart against the enemy's negativity, and filling your spirit with God's Word.

Father, thank You for the encouragement of Your Word to do what is right. Guide and direct my steps toward healthy living.

—— DAY 7: REFLECTION AND APPLICATION
Lord, keep my glance in a looking up posture, so that I see others as You see them— worthy of love and care.

When we face challenges in our lives, we often skew what the truth actually is—making things worse in our minds than they actually are. We might even begin believing lies of the enemy. Jenn Hand offers some lie-slayers in a blog she wrote, excerpted here in parts:[3]

Lie #1: I shouldn't have to endure this pain.

Truth: Suffering is part of human existence. None of us is immune to it, but we can have peace in the midst of it by trusting God has a greater plan at work.

Scripture: "I have told you these things, so that in me you may have peace. In this world you will have trouble. But, take heart! I have overcome the world." (John 16:33)

"And we know that in all things God works for the good of those who love him, who have been called according to his purpose." (Romans 8:28)

Lie #2: I am a burden to others.

Truth: Being in physical or emotional pain doesn't make you needy, annoying, or helpless—it makes you human.

Scripture: "Carry each other's burdens, and in this way you will fulfill the law of Christ." (Galatians 6:2)

"Come to me, all you who are weary and burdened, and I will give you rest. Take my yoke upon you and learn from me, for I am gentle and humble in heart, and you will find rest for your souls. For my yoke is easy and my burden is light." (Matthew 11:28-30)

Lie #3: I'll never be able to fulfill God's calling for me now.

Truth: God doesn't make mistakes. This is His plan for me. I can either learn from and grow through the struggle, or I can try to run from or fast forward through it. The latter will leave me frustrated and exhausted, and I could miss what God has for me here. The former will draw me into the arms of my Savior, where I will be transformed.

Scripture: "Not only so, but we also glory in our sufferings, because we know that suffering produces perseverance; perseverance, character; and character, hope. And hope does not put us to shame, because God's love has been poured out into our hearts through the Holy Spirit, who has been given to us." (Romans 5:3-5)

"I will go before you and will level the mountains; I will break down gates of bronze and cut through bars of iron. I will give you the treasures of darkness, riches stored in secret places, so that you may know that I am the LORD, the God of Israel, who summons you by name." (Isaiah 45:2-3)

We often cannot change our circumstances, but we can change our mindset. That doesn't mean we slip into hopelessness. On the contrary we shift to a hopeful perspective, because we know God is with us in that challenge as we hand over the control to him.

We also do not necessarily give up and do nothing. As we have learned in this week's lesson, when we listen carefully to the voice of the Lord our God, do what is right in His sight, and obey Him, we will sense whether or not we should wait for Him to work out the details or take specific action.

Write this week's memory verse here:

_____

_____

_____

What does this promise speak to you about a challenge that is currently facing you?

_____

_____

_____

[1] Neurohealth Associates, "Neuroscience Reveals: Gratitude Literally Rewires Your Brain to Be Happy," Neurohealth. 4 July 2020. https://nhahealth.com/neuroscience-reveals-gratitude-literally-rewires-your-brain-to-be-happier/

[2] Amy Gray, "Amy Gray." First Place for Health, Hope Stories. 2022. https://www.firstplaceforhealth.com/amy-gray/.

[3] Jenn Hand, "How to Change Your Mindset When You Can't Change Your Situation." Dr. Michelle Bengston Hope Prevails. 31 Jan. 2022. https://drmichellebengtson.com/change-mindset-when-cant-change-situation/. Additional help can be found in Bengston's book Breaking Anxiety's Grip: How to Reclaim the Peace God Promises (Grand Rapids: Revell, 2019).

WEEK THREE: FROM HURTS TO HEALING

SCRIPTURE MEMORY VERSE
And he said to Moses, "Please, my lord, do not hold against us the sin we have so foolishly committed." Numbers 12:11

For some of us the bondage we may be under may relate to broken relationships. We may not be able to move forward into wellness, because our hearts are broken or we are simply holding onto unforgiveness and even anger due to past offenses against us. This has been true for me.

In late 2001 our mountain valley, where my husband is a cattle rancher, experienced a two-day blizzard with a tremendous amount of snow. That snow covered over six calves that had bedded down with an old bull in a dry creek bed in a far corner of the ranch. He first learned of this with a knock on the door and a deputy sheriff arresting him for six felony counts of animal cruelty. A neighbor who had a grudge against my husband (because he wouldn't sell the neighbor a strip of land) had called animal control.

While it took three-and-a-half years for that case to get to trial, we were not concerned because all the evidence was on our side. Auction records showed top dollar prices for his cattle. Necropsies of the two animals examined showed one had twenty pounds of feed in its stomach and the other had a high level of colostrum—in other words, they had been well fed. Two large veterinarians agreed Craig had not been negligent. And the chief beef expert at the UC Davis School of Veterinary Science would testify in Craig's behalf.

However, the trial became a mockery of justice. The judge refused to allow those auction records as evidence at trial. He openly harassed defense witnesses, even the doctors. And he would not allow the vet professor to testify. Consequently, Craig was convicted of those felonies and then sentenced to four years of probation and a large fine.

For most of the next two years, he and I worked on an appeal that showed more than two hundred instances of prejudice and waited for it to be heard at the California

Court of Appeals. In January 2007 the three appellate judges overturned the decision. While we won that case, the emotional losses paid a huge toll on our lives. Over and over again we find we still have to forgive that judge; the district attorney, who should have been seeking justice rather than conviction (he never interviewed defense witnesses before the trial); and even the jurors.

Healing from injustice, abuse, and cruelties requires the difficult task of forgiveness, which takes time. But because forgiveness is a hallmark of the Christian faith, it is a necessary part of every believer's journey toward wholeness. And we can see its importance in the lives of three Exodus siblings: Moses, Aaron, and Miriam.

—— DAY 1: IDENTIFYING THE ISSUE

Lord God, You well know of the relational breach I am experiencing with someone who matters to me. Help me recognize and understand the truth.

Even the closest of relationships can experience bumps in a life's journey. An unkind remark can create a chasm that seemingly widens as years go by. Selfishness can make us feel belittled and unvalued. Abuse destroys our trust in those who should be trustworthy. Jealousies can crop up too, as we see in Moses's family.

After the Israelites had made it through the Red Sea and through initial struggles to trust God for water and sustenance, Moses's two older siblings began to grumble against their brother.

Read Numbers 12:1-16.

What was Miriam and Aaron's initial complaint of Moses (see 12:1)?

What was the true, underlying issue they were having (see 12:2)?

What was the Lord's response to their remarks (see 12:4)?

_____

_____

_____

Summarize what the Lord said to Aaron and Miriam (see 12:6-8).

_____

_____

_____

Now explain what three actions the Lord took after speaking to them (see 12:9-10).

_____

_____

_____

Why was the Lord so angry, do you think (see 12:3, 6-8)?

_____

_____

_____

Aaron and Miriam initially complained about Moses's marriage to a Cushite woman, who would have come from the southern Nile valley and may have had deeply tanned skin. This woman was probably not Zipporah, the Midianite daughter of the priest Reuel (also called Jethro), who may have died. Underlying those grumbles, though, was a streak of jealousy in Aaron and Miriam—that Moses was in power and they were not as influential. Moses was the leader of the older two, and they couldn't find fault with his leadership. So they attacked him on a personal level.

Sometimes we do that too or find ourselves victim of others' unwarranted criticism. In those times we will be well served to understand underlying feelings that have fueled emotional responses.

How have you been hurt by someone recently?

_____

_____

_____

What, do you think, is the underlying reason for this person's words or actions? How could this help you gain perspective on the situation?

_____

_____

_____

Lord God, help me understand what may be underlying this offense, and give me the grace not to respond in kind.

—— DAY 2: UNDERSTANDING

Lord, when someone hurts me, help me remember the best of our relationship. Amen.

Moses was not the oldest sibling in the family. Aaron was the oldest, and Miriam was the middle child. Moses owed a great debt to both of them.

Read Exodus 1:22. What was Pharaoh's edict?

_____

_____

_____

Now read Exodus 2:1-10. When Moses was born, what did his mother do (2:2-4)? Who was watching over Moses?

_____

_____

_____

While not named in this text, the sister is Miriam. How is Moses discovered?

_____

_____

_____

Who steps forward to help and what is her suggestion?

_____

_____

_____

The best of the possible worlds happens for baby Moses, who is described as a "fine child" (Exodus 2:2) and "no ordinary child" (Acts 7:20; Hebrews 11:23). One commentary says, "The account of Moses' remarkable deliverance in infancy foreshadows the deliverance from Egypt that God would later effect through him."[1] As God would later swoop away the Red Sea waters to deliver the Israelites from captivity and probable death, Miriam swept Moses away to his mother—her mother, Jochebed—to nurse her own child. And not only that, Pharaoh's daughter would provide payment. After the nursing period (probably about three years) ended, Pharaoh's daughter took Moses to the royal home to be raised.

Ponder this a bit. How might these circumstances have influenced Moses's perception of his sister Miriam?

_____

_____

_____

What is the context of the conflict that you have had with the person mentioned on Day 1? How might thinking through your history with this person help you shift toward a posture of healing?

_____

_____

_____

Lord God, provide a great measure of grace to me as I process the hurt I have experienced. Amen.

—— DAY 3: REMEMBERING

Lord, when I am feeling offended, remind me of those times that person has supported me. Amen.

While it was Miriam who experienced the brunt of the consequences for her and Aaron's criticism of Moses, Aaron seemingly was just as guilty. Today we will again step back in time a bit to review the history between Moses and Aaron in their partnership to petition Pharaoh to release the captive Israelites into freedom and how they had worked together. Let's examine this partnership to understand better their relationship.

Read Exodus 4:13-16. After Moses again asks the Lord to send someone else to approach Pharaoh, how did God suggest Moses would partner with his brother?

_____

_____

_____

Now read Exodus 4:27:27-31 and answer these questions. Who set up the meeting between Moses and Aaron (see 4:27)? What transpired at that meeting (see 4:28)?

_____
_____
_____

Who set up the meeting between the brothers and the Israelite elders (see 4:29)? Who did the speaking and performed the signs (see 4:30)?

_____
_____
_____

And how did the elders respond (see 4:31)?

_____
_____
_____

What kind of relationship do you feel Moses and Aaron had at this juncture of their lives?

_____
_____
_____

In the following scriptures indicate who is doing the speaking or the action. The first one is done for you.

REFERENCE	MOSES AND/OR AARON?	NAME OF OTHER PARTY IN CONVERSATION/ ACTION
Exodus 5:1,3	Moses and Aaron	Pharaoh
Exodus 5:22		
Exodus 7:19-20		
Exodus 8:5-6		

Exodus 12:31-32		
Exodus 12:43,50		

Imagine Moses and Aaron going through these experiences together. Was either of them greater than the other, do you think? Explain your answer.

_____

_____

_____

How do you think relationships break down?

_____

_____

_____

In regard to a broken relationship you've had with a family, friend, or co-worker, how did that relationship change for the worse?

_____

_____

_____

It may be that the hurt with which you struggle relates to your being abused. This Bible study may help somewhat, but you may need other kinds of counseling and support to find a process of healing. Mary DeMuth is one author who advocates for empathy and care for those who have been abused.

> When I tell my story, some recoil from it, no doubt wishing I would just be quiet and not speak of the past. Sexual abuse and trauma are painful, and the shame of those experiences thrives in darkness. One sad truth I've learned over the years is that the church doesn't like messy. The church prefers a neat, victorious story, tied up with a cliché bow, full of manufactured piety and pasted on "joy." Seldom is there room for questions, wrestling, anguish, grief, or bewilderment—because that somehow connotes that those who were harmed are not "walking in faith."[2]

If your church has not been a safe place for you to get help, you can call the National Domestic Hotline at 1-800-799-7233.

Father, help me seek the healing that I need from the hurts I have experienced. Amen.

—— DAY 4: FINDING THE CAUSE

Lord, when a relationship breaks down, help me to figure out the root cause and what I may have done to contribute to that situation. Amen.

There seems to be a change in the family dynamics when the Israelites come up against the Red with Pharaoh's army bearing down on them. In the next couple of chapters of Exodus we see Moses taking charge, without mention of Aaron.

In the following scenes, who is doing the speaking or leading the people?

REFERENCE	SCENE	WHO IS LEADING OR SPEAKING?
Exodus 13:1-3	Consecration of the firstborn	
Exodus 14:13-14	Complaints of Israelites	
Exodus 14:21	Parting of Red Sea	
Exodus 14:26-27	Reversal of Red Sea	
Exodus 15:1, 20-21	Celebration Worship	
Exodus 15:24-25	Water Purification Miracle	

For these several dramatic chapters, we do not see or hear from Aaron. He very well may have continued to remain with Moses at the lead position of the Exodus. Or he may have helped motivate the rest of the group from the rear. As a former educator who took students on many field trips, I know that the aides who ushered along the stragglers in the back were much more important than I, who walked in front of the group going at a quick clip. However, because Moses had fully taken the reins of the journey at this point and was the key figure in following God's orchestration of the Red Sea and the water purification miracles, the Israelites very well may have begun to see Moses in a holy light.

Aaron does step back into the picture when the Israelites begin complaining for food. Read Exodus 16:2-3. To whom are the people complaining?

_____

_____

_____

To whom does the Lord give instructions in Exodus 16:4?

_____

_____

_____

Who speaks to the Israelites in Exodus 16:6?

_____

_____

_____

Who gives instructions in Exodus 16:9? Then who speaks to the Israelites in Exodus 16:10?

_____

_____

_____

When tension rises and external forces put pressure on a person, that extra burden can affect relationships between the people involved. For example, when finances are slim, married couples can have arguments about spending priorities. When an employer tells an employee that she must work overtime to take care of a last-minute project on deadline, tension can occur not only in that workplace between those individuals but also between those workers and their spouses at home.

What are triggers in your home or work life that tend to bring about tension in your relationships?

_____

_____

_____

External pressures can cause us to make bad choices not only in relationships but also in regard to our health. How to you respond?

_____

_____

_____

Lord, help me respond in a godly manner when tension rises—with my words and with my actions. Amen

—— DAY 5: FORGIVING

Father, help me not only to forgive but also to take measurable steps to restore a relationship. Amen.

It is shortly after this that Miriam and Aaron criticize their brother Moses about his Cushite wife and then infer their jealousy over Moses's rise to leadership. The scripture tells us "at once" the Lord stepped in, confronted Aaron and Miriam about their critical attitudes toward their brother, and caused Miriam to become leprous.

Read Numbers 12:9-16.

There is some controversy over the word that is translated *leprous*. There is little evidence that leprosy, also called Hansen's disease, existed to any substantial degree in the ancient Near East.

> "Examinations of skeletal remains from both Egypt and Israel show little evidence of the bone deformities typically caused by leprosy; the earliest indication of true leprosy in Egypt dates to the early Christian period. The Hebrew term metsoraat, often translated as "leprosy," most likely refers to changes in the skin that result from any number of dermatological conditions (e.g., psoriasis, eczema), fungal infections (e.g., ringworm), or other causes."[2]

Scripture says Miriam stood "leprous, like snow" (Numbers 12:10). Certainly, her appearance was meant to startle and repulse anyone who saw her, and as this occurred immediately after God's chastisement of her and Aaron, her condition clearly indicated God's judgment.

How does Aaron react (see 12:10-12)? What does he say to Moses?

_____

_____

_____

And how does Moses respond (see 12:13)? What is his apparent emotion?

_____

_____

_____

How does the Lord respond to Moses (see 12:14)?

_____

_____

_____

It was a ritual that exposure to bodily fluids or uncleanness required a seven-day period of isolation from the rest of the community. Despite Moses's quick forgiveness of his sister's criticism and even his advocacy to the Lord in her behalf, she must live out her consequences. Clearly, Aaron must have also felt shame that his sister bore punishment that he also deserved. In any case, this incident stalls the progress of the Israelites in their journey through the desert, as they could not move on "till she was brought back" (Numbers 12:15).

Sometimes when two people have a conflict, there are others who are affected by their broken relationship. Recall a time when perhaps others you care about also experienced stress and hurt because of the conflict you experienced.

_____

_____

_____

Pray this prayer for those on the sidelines:

Lord, I regret the brokenness of this relationship and ask that You help bring about restoration not only with this other person but also with others who may have been on the sidelines. Amen.

—— DAY 6: REFLECTION AND APPLICATION

Father, help me to live a live that demonstrates mercy and grace, because You have extended both abundantly to me. Amen.

My husband Craig and I were sitting outside the courtroom when the jury approached us. As they looked at us before going back into the courtroom doors, disgust appeared on their faces, and my gut instantly knew the news would not be good.

Despite the jurors' foreshadowing, it was still a shock to hear the jury foreman announce "guilty" to six of the felonies. And while we won the appeal, we still felt the effects of pain and loss of five-and-a-half years of our lives. A judge, the jury, and a district attorney who never interviewed any defense witnesses had stolen much from us, and we remained emotionally and mentally bruised and even angry.

One personal struggle was the fact that we live in a town of 800 people in a county of only around 3,000. One of the jurors was the business manager for the school district in which I worked. Another was a woman who had often substituted for me in my classroom. The head juror was the son of a woman with whom I had prayer-walked. And as the school academic advisor, I had to work with the district attorney for Rotary scholarships for high school students—a person I never wanted to see again.

A few months after we had won the appeal, Craig and I went to a Rotary fundraiser event. Going out in public was still painful for me at that time, but I wanted to show support for an organization that had helped so many of my students, including my own children. As I began talking to a friend, I watched as my husband approached the district attorney and began talking to him in a congenial matter.

As the all-too-familiar nausea hit me again, it struck me that if my husband could forgive someone who had wronged us so deeply, so could I. However, I must be honest. The pain of injustice doesn't always disappear completely. It would be helpful if I could have selective amnesia! But those memories are still vivid, and as I find them surfacing again and again, I pray, "Lord, once more I forgive the judge, the jury, and the D.A. Let not a root of bitterness bind its way around my heart and through my soul."

As you consider someone who has hurt you, write a similar kind of prayer here...and pray.

_____

_____

_____

Heavenly Father, thank You for the example of Your Son Jesus, whose first of three prayers that we have in Your Word was, "Father, forgive them, for they know not what they do." May I always quickly forgive and trust You for the outcome. In Jesus's name, amen.

—— DAY 7: REFLECTION AND APPLICATION

Father, help me find practical ways to restore broken relationships, so that I live out a faith-filled life that honors you. Amen.

Unforgiveness can weigh us down. Its anger, bitterness, and even anxiety can create headaches, stomach aches, and chest pain. It can also cause us to eat comfort foods that pack on the pounds and make us feel even worse. Conversely, forgiving someone—whether he or she has sought reconciliation or accepted blame—can free us from emotional chains. At least once a year I taught my high school students about forgiveness, typically when I'd hear the expression, "He makes me so mad!" And I would explain how forgiveness helps us move forward with our lives.

Even the Mayo Clinic would agree, as we can find in a long article about the subject. It argues that harboring anger and bitterness can affect other relationships, a lack of appreciation for the present, the loss of joy from new experiences, anxiety, depression, a feeling that your life lacks purpose or meaning, and a loss of connectedness with others. You might even develop a lack of distrust for people in general—not just those who have hurt you—and become unwilling to enter into new relationships or to try new experiences.

Letting go of bitterness and anger can lead to the following:

- Healthier relationships
- Improved mental health
- Less anxiety, stress, and hostility
- Lower blood pressure
- Fewer symptoms of depression
- A stronger immune system
- Improved heart health
- Improved self-esteem

Forgiveness is something we can do—even when we don't feel like it—and there are steps we can take that are healthy for breakthrough in relationships and for ourselves as well.

- Recognize that forgiveness can be good not only for the relationship but also for ourselves.
- Identify underlying issues that may have pre-existed the offense.
- Consider joining a faith-based small group.
- Talk to a counselor or pastor
- Shift our mindset from that of victim to someone who is proactive and trusting God for the situation and ultimate results.
- Practice empathy by trying to see the situation from the other person's perspective.
- Reflect on times you have hurt others and those who have forgiven you.
- Write out your feelings in a letter...and throw it away rather than send it.
- Talk with a single trusted friend who could help process the situation and provide objective perspective.
- Give it over in prayer to God. Repeat. Repeat. Repeat.

In Matthew 18:21-22 Peter asks Jesus, "Lord, how many times shall I forgive my brother or sister who sins against me? Up to seven times?"

Jesus answers, "I tell you, not seven times, but seventy-seven times."

This passage syncs well with this sentence in the Lord's prayer: "Forgive us our debts, as we also have forgiven our debtors" (Matthew 6:12). Each day throws new opportunities at us to exercise biblical forgiveness as we respond to offenses from those we love, from sources on social media, and from folks we don't even know. Every time we make a choice to refuse to be offended, we experience breakthrough in our lives—breakthrough that will also pay off as we determine not to let our emotions detour us into unhealthy choices.

How will you respond the next time someone offends you?

_____
_____
_____

[1]*The NIV Study Bible*. Ed. Kenneth Barker. (Grand Rapids: Zondervan, 1985), 88-89.
[2]Mary DeMuth, "Why I Wrote We Too." MaryDeMuth.com. 13 Aug. 2019. https://www.marydemuth.com/why-i-wrote-we-too/.
[3]*NIV Cultural Backgrounds Study Bible*. (Grand Rapids: Zondervan, 2016), 111.
[4]Mayo Clinic Staff, "Forgiveness: Letting Go of Grudges and Bitterness." Mayo Clinic, 13 Nov. 2020. https://www.mayoclinic.org/healthy-lifestyle/adult-health/in-depth/forgiveness/art-20047692#:~:text=If%20you're%20truly%20sorry,forgiveness%20in%20their%20own%20time.

WEEK FOUR: FROM OVERWHELMED TO ORGANIZED

SCRIPTURE MEMORY VERSE
The Lord answered Moses, "Is the Lord's arm too short? You will now see whether or not what I say will come true for you." Numbers 11:23

You have probably heard the expression "God won't give you more than you can bear." Actually, that idea is not expressed in the Bible. People often take a verse out of context. The verse cited is "No temptation has overtaken you except what is common to mankind. And God is faithful; he will not let you be tempted beyond what you can bear. But when you are tempted, he will also provide a way out so that you can endure it" (1 Corinthians 10:13 NIV). That scripture clearly pertains to temptation, not to life's overwhelming circumstances.

I can remember one Easter when I felt overwhelmed with responsibility and lost sight of the joy of that day. I helped with the Easter sunrise service, co-coordinated a joint-church community breakfast, sang with the choir during the service, led the junior church activities, and then fixed a full Easter dinner for company at our home. Tension over getting all those activities just right carried over into a less-than-hospitable attitude toward my husband and our four kids—certainly not a celebratory focus for Resurrection Day.

The truth is that sometimes we allow situations to build up and overwhelm us, because we have mismanaged our time or taken on too many responsibilities that were never meant for us to do. We also may also not have a good sense of how to strategize and organize the tangibles of life—our homes, our workplaces, and even our health and meal planning. Then when life's details stack up and overwhelm us, we make poor choices that affect our well-being and that of those we love.

Even Moses got a little skewed with his mission and purpose, as we will study this week.

—— DAY 1: ASSESSING THE PROBLEM
Lord God, help me understand how to manage my life, so that I do not have an unfavorable witness and so that You are glorified.

Apparently, sometime after the Exodus Moses had sent his wife Zipporah and their sons to her father Jethro with the news that the Exodus mission had been successful. Then Jethro returned with them and visited his son-in-law.

Read Exodus 18:7-14. While "Jethro was delighted to hear about all the good things the Lord had done for Israel," he did note a problem. What was that situation that was affecting Moses (see v. 14)?

_____

_____

_____

Why do you think Jethro made this observation?

_____

_____

_____

Read Exodus 18:15-16. How did Moses answer him?

_____

_____

_____

At this point in the story, it was three months after the Israelites had left Egypt. With millions now on the road to the Promised Land, conflicts certainly were a given, but Moses was the only one who had assumed responsibility for making judgments to settle those disputes. How do you think this was affecting Moses and perhaps even his family?

_____

_____

_____

How would you respond if someone made a comment to you such as the one Jethro said to Moses?

_____

_____

_____

Recall a time when you felt overwhelmed by responsibility. What was that situation? What typically builds up to create that scenario in your life?

_____

_____

_____

And how do you usually respond?

_____

_____

_____

Who is a Jethro figure for you now—someone who could give you sound counsel when you clearly are overwhelmed? How does that person help you?

_____

_____

_____

Lord, thank you for those You put into my life who can come alongside me when I am overwhelmed and help me assess why.

—— DAY 2: REMEMBERING YOUR MISSION
Lord God, when I get overwhelmed, remind me of Your calling on my life and point out that which is not meant for me.

One reason we often feel overwhelmed may be that we have taken on responsibilities we were never meant to have. In coaching new writers, I often hear, "I know God has called me to write a book, but I have a hard time finding time to write." The truth is this: God does not call us to do anything for which he does not equip us and for which we do not have time. The likelihood is that we fill our schedules with responsibilities for which we were never meant to be responsible.

In yesterday's lesson we saw that Moses's father-in-law noticed that Moses was worn out with the burden of managing complaints. Today we will revisit the scene of the burning bush and the call that God originally put on Moses's life.

Read Exodus 3:7-10. God saw the great need of His people in Egypt. What was that need (see vv. 7, 9)?

_____

_____

_____

What was God's plan (see v. 8)?

_____

_____

_____

What did God tell Moses to do (see v. 10)?

_____

_____

_____

With any migration of a large number of people, there would be numerous concerns a leader might have to undertake. What would be some of those?

_____

_____

_____

The call on Moses's life was not easy. Moses had to leave Midian on the northeast side of the Red Sea to go back westward to Egypt—a place from where he had fled. Then the Israelites were resentful when Pharaoh made their work harder after he rejected Moses's request to let them go. And of course, there was the series of ten plagues and then the urgency of leaving after the final plague on the firstborn and the Passover.

While a calling from God may have one central purpose, there may be other attendant roles and tasks one might have to take. Moses's call to lead the people out of Egypt involved numerous requests to Pharaoh, directions to the Israelites about the Passover, and conversations with God about how to provide water and food. Eventually, though, Moses got to a place where he was overwhelmed with administrative and even judicial tasks, as Jethro pointed out.

Think of something you know God has called you to do. What various tasks were or have been involved in that calling, including some that you did not initially expect?

_____

_____

_____

Part of life coaching involves helping others examine the various roles and responsibilities in their life and then assessing what ones are not within their life's purposes. For example, when one woman found that her life's purpose is to teach, she found it fairly simple to decide to discontinue two different volunteer activities so she was more focused on her calling.

What responsibilities do you now have that you would like to and could realistically let go?

_____

_____

_____

One important role we must assume is to take care of our health. What practical steps could you take to make sure you are eating foods that are healthy and to commit to consistent exercise?

_____

_____

_____

Father, when I get overwhelmed, often I am the one who has overcommitted myself and even taken on responsibilities You never handed to me. Help me establish clear priorities and boundaries, so that I am focused and following Your will.

—— DAY 3: DELEGATING

Lord, show me how to simplify my life by learning to delegate tasks. I know this involves releasing control and trusting others, but I can do all that by looking to You first.

Sometimes others can see ways we can simplify our lives better than we can. Often we do not necessarily appreciate unsolicited advice, but sometimes if it is couched in love and concern, we can receive it well. Jethro provided sound counsel to his son-in-law Moses.

Read Exodus 18:17-23. What are several reasons Jethro is concerned (see vv. 17-18)?

_____

_____

_____

In verse 19 how does Jethro couch or soften his comment that he will give advice to Moses?

_____

_____

_____

What are the four pieces of advice Jethro gives to Moses?

Verse 19	
Verse 20	
Verse 21	
Verse 22	

Essentially, Jethro encouraged Moses to appoint others to serve as officials and judges. What would be the desired outcome for both the people and for Moses (see v. 22)?

_____

_____

_____

Read Exodus 18:24-27. How did Moses follow through and what results ensued before Jethro returned home?

_____

_____

_____

What lessons can we glean from this important chapter?

_____

_____

_____

Is it simple or difficult for you to delegate tasks? Why?

_____

_____

_____

When you do delegate responsibilities, what are generally the results and how do you feel afterwards?

_____

_____

_____

Yesterday you listed one or more responsibility that you could release to simplify your life. How and when will you do that? Who could competently take over this for you?

_____

_____

_____

When we let go of tasks, sometimes they or others creep back into our schedules, bringing us to that same place of feeling overwhelmed. What kinds of questions could you ask yourself to prevent this from happening?

_____

_____

_____

Father, I have many expectations made of me that oftentimes weigh me down. Help me eliminate those roles or tasks so that I am not exhausted and joy-depleted, as I simply want to follow Your lead in my life.

—— DAY 4: LISTENING

Lord, moving from a place of being overwhelmed to a place of structure and organization takes a listening ear. Speak, Lord, for your servant is listening.

Unfortunately, Moses found himself back in the same position of being overwhelmed just two years later. In Numbers 10 we learn the Israelites left the Sinai peninsula, which sticks down from the north into the Red Sea, in the cloud of God's protection for the Desert of Paran. This was often called the wilderness, where the wanderings took place. In the wilderness "the people complained about their hardships in the hearing of the Lord" (Numbers 11:1), and the Lord responded with literal fire among them and on the camp outskirts. When the people cried out to Moses, he prayed to the Lord and the fire died down.

Then the people complained again. Read Numbers 11:4-10. What were the people's complaints (see vv. 4-6)?

_____

_____

_____

How did the Lord respond to these complaints (see v. 10)? Why, do you think?

_____

_____

_____

Moses also was troubled that the people were not appreciative of their daily provision of food to sustain them for the journey. And once more, Moses was overwhelmed. What are some of Moses's questions for God in Numbers 11:11-13)?

_____

_____

_____

Whereas before it was Jethro who noticed Moses was feeling burdened, this time Moses felt his limits and was burdened. Read Numbers 11:14-15. What specifically does Moses say he cannot handle?

_____

_____

_____

And what does he ask God to do?

_____

_____

_____

What do you think Moses needs? What could have helped him before he got to a desperate place of feeling life wasn't worth living?

_____

_____

_____

What situations in your life tend to yo-yo and frustrate you? Your weight? Exercise regimens? Household organization? Finances?

_____

_____

_____

What would help you maintain good routines?

_____

_____

_____

Lord, I truly do want to stay in routines that are good for me. Help me stay the course with my schedule, my routines, and my health.

—— DAY 5: MAKING ADJUSTMENTS

Lord, help me develop disciplines in my life that will spill over into my physical, mental, emotional, and spiritual health.

When life gets too full, it's hard to keep closets and cupboards organized, but it's also hard to keep calm and collected. While physical clutter can take over surfaces of a home, mental, and emotional clutter can burden us also. Life's surprises—as simple as a broken-down refrigerator or car—can weigh down an already full to-do list. Then when others in the family have significant needs or a rotten attitude, we might feel overwhelmed as Moses did. And those situations affect our attitudes and the ways we behave toward others.

What did the Lord tell Moses to do in Numbers 11:16-17?

_____

_____

_____

And what did the Lord say to tell the people in Numbers 11:18-20?

_____

_____

_____

How did Moses reply in Numbers 11:21-22? What do you think was his attitude?

_____

_____

_____

The Lord replied, "Is the Lord's arm too short? You will now see whether or not what I say will come true for you" (Numbers 11:23). Like Moses, we see life through our human lenses, forgetting that we serve a God who can do the impossible—such as part a sea or make food appear out of nothing.

Read Numbers 11:24-25. How did Moses follow through?

_____

_____

_____

It is somewhat comforting to read about biblical heroes of the faith who demonstrated moments of frustration, weakness, and even desperation. From them we can learn perspective about our own weak points and challenge ourselves to do better.

One good practice is to recognize our limits. When we are too busy to prepare and eat healthy foods, our schedule is probably too full. When we don't have time to exercise, something else probably should go by the wayside. And if we cannot objectively make those decisions, it's time to go to God in prayer and ask Him for his direction. In other words, it's time to slow down a bit, seek the Lord, listen, and then make adjustments.

One of those adjustments is to remember a principle taught in this week's memory verse. Write that from memory here:

_____

_____

_____

What adjustment in thinking do you sense God is asking you to make that would help you move from a feeling of being overwhelmed to one of organization?

Lord, guide me clearly in Your purpose for my life, so that I do not get overwhelmed by tasks never meant for me.

—— DAY 6: REFLECTION AND APPLICATION
Lord, I truly want to depend on You for everything I have and even everything I eat. Guide and direct my health steps.

We learn principles about God's provision and even hoarding from the desert wanderings of the Israelites in Exodus 16. When the people grumbled about food, the Lord told Moses he would "rain down bread from heaven" for them but that the people were only to gather enough manna for one day at a time (Exodus 16:4). On the sixth day only could they gather for that day and the Sabbath rest day.

Several principles about trusting God for our food and our possessions can be found from in Exodus 16. First, you'll read the scripture, then you'll read the principle we can draw from that scripture. Here is what Moses and Aaron told the Israelites in Exodus 16:

> "In the evening you will know that it was the LORD who brought you out of Egypt, and in the morning you will see the glory of the LORD, because he has heard your grumbling against him. Who are we, that you should grumble against us?" Moses also said, "You will know that it was the LORD when he gives you meat to eat in the evening and all the bread you want in the morning, because he has heard your grumbling against him. Who are we? You are not grumbling against us, but against the LORD." (vv. 6-8)

Principal #1: When we complain because of not having enough of something, we are grumbling against the Lord. God gives us what we need.

That evening quail came and covered the camp, and in the morning there was a layer of dew around the camp. When the dew was gone, thin flakes like frost on the ground appeared on the desert floor. When the Israelites saw it, they said to each other, "What is it?" For they did not know what it was.

Moses said to them, "It is the bread the LORD has given you to eat. This is what the LORD has commanded: 'Everyone is to gather as much as they need. Take an omer for each person you have in your tent.'"

The Israelites did as they were told; some gathered much, some little. And when they measured it by the omer, the one who gathered much did not have too much, and the one who gathered little did not have too little. Everyone had gathered just as much as they needed. (vv. 13-18)

Principal #2: Foods that are healthy for us may not be the foods we indulged in from our past—those that got us into weight and other health struggles. Just as God gave the Israelites food that would sustain them—manna (and later quail)—we may need to abandon past practices of eating foods that create cravings and learn to embrace those that are good for us.

Then Moses said to them, "No one is to keep any of it until morning."

However, some of them paid no attention to Moses; they kept part of it until morning, but it was full of maggots and began to smell. So Moses was angry with them. (vv. 19-20)

Principal #3: Hoarding food (and overeating) will eventually bite us—if not physically, then possibly financially. Food is expensive, and buying too much can often mean it goes to waste (if not waist).

Each morning everyone gathered as much as they needed, and when the sun grew hot, it melted away. On the sixth day, they gathered twice as much—two omers for each person—and the leaders of the community came and reported this to Moses. He said to them, "This is what the LORD commanded: 'Tomorrow is to be a day of sabbath rest, a holy sabbath to the LORD. So bake what you want to bake and boil what you want to boil. Save whatever is left and keep it until morning.'"

So they saved it until morning, as Moses commanded, and it did not stink or get maggots in it. "Eat it today," Moses said, "because today is a sabbath to the LORD. You will not find any of it on the ground today. Six days you are to gather it, but on the seventh day, the Sabbath, there will not be any."

Nevertheless, some of the people went out on the seventh day to gather it, but they found none. Then the LORD said to Moses, "How long will you refuse to keep my commands and my instructions? Bear in mind that the LORD has given you the Sabbath; that is why on the sixth day he gives you bread for two days. Everyone is to stay where they are on the seventh day; no one is to go out." So the people rested on the seventh day. (vv. 21-30)

Principal #4: Planning is important for healthy living. When we don't make healthy meal plans and purchases, we might develop a grab-and-go plan of fast food that doesn't fuel our bodies well.

The people of Israel called the bread manna. It was white like coriander seed and tasted like wafers made with honey. Moses said, "This is what the LORD has commanded: 'Take an omer of manna and keep it for the generations to come, so they can see the bread I gave you to eat in the wilderness when I brought you out of Egypt.'"

So Moses said to Aaron, "Take a jar and put an omer of manna in it. Then place it before the LORD to be kept for the generations to come."

As the LORD commanded Moses, Aaron put the manna with the tablets of the covenant law, so that it might be preserved. The Israelites ate manna forty years, until they came to a land that was settled; they ate manna until they reached the border of Canaan. (vv. 31-35)

Principle #5: Share with others God's success stories of provision in your life. You don't need to have a jar of manna to remind you, but you will find that speaking of the Lord's faithfulness is also a good reminder to continue to trust Him for exactly what you need—food and other needs.

What have you learned from Exodus 16 about how God views our daily needs and/
or possessions?

_____

_____

_____

*Father God, thank You for providing just what I need just when I need it. Forgive me
for overindulging at times and for not trusting You at other times. You are my Jehovah
Jireh—my God Who Provides.*

—— DAY 7: REFLECTION AND APPLICATION
*Lord, help me develop organized systems in my life that will help me thrive physically,
mentally, emotionally, and even spiritually.*

As the book of Numbers begins, the Israelites had been camped out at Mount Sinai
(at the southern region of the Sinai Peninsula) for about a year after the Exodus.
There they had received all the laws and regulations recorded in the book of Leviticus. Expectations for behavior and obedience were established. Then the Lord told
Moses, "Take a census of the whole Israelite community by their clans and families,
listing every man by name, one by one" (Numbers 1:2).

Next God laid out a second major organizational strategy: "The Israelites are to
camp around the tent of meeting some distance from it, each of them under their
standard and holding the banners of their family" (Numbers 2:1 NIV). The Lord's
specific instructions included a pattern for how the twelve tribes would camp around
the tabernacle and how they would march forward. They did not camp or proceed in
a random fashion; there was a plan for how they were ordered.

One principal we gain from these initial chapters of Numbers is that we follow a God
of order. One reason we often feel overwhelmed is that we cannot find things in our
home and office spaces because of the physical clutter of our lives. The National
Association of Professional Organizers states that Americans collectively waste nine
million hours daily searching for misplaced items, and "nearly a quarter of us admit
to paying late penalties because we've lost bills."[1] Getting organized can help us find
that lost time to track the food we are eating and get the exercise we think we might
otherwise think we don't have time for.

A few years ago I watched a couple home improvement shows of professional organizers and decided to work systematically through my home to simplify it and create
workable systems to keep it organized. Kathi Lipp, author of *The Clutter-Free Home:*

Making Room for Your Life, suggests we ask ourselves three questions as we make functional and practical zones in our homes:

- Do I love it?
- Do I use it?
- Would I buy it again?[2]

Simplifying our homes makes it easier to make decisions, such as with a wardrobe. If we have only clothing that we love, that fits, and that looks good on us, it's easier to decide what to wear instead of wading through oceans of items that are simply taking up space.

Ordering a home is not hard. Here are some ideas to consider

- Start with the mindset that this is doable. Any messy space can be simplified and organized. It may take a little time, but the whole process may not take as much time as you think.

- Also consider that if you believe God has provided your home, you do not need more than what will comfortably fit in its spaces, and you probably can downsize much of what you have. Kathi Lipp has written that she and her husband first got rid of half of their belongings with one move and then half of that amount when they moved again. I have taken the view, for example, that I do not need more books than what will fit on the three bookshelves in my office, so I continually give away books after I read them.

- Choose a single zone (a closet, a cupboard, a drawer, a surface of furniture such as the top of a dresser) to work on at a time.

- Remove everything from that space and clean it before putting anything else back.

- Examine each item you've removed, one at a time, asking yourself the three questions above.

- Then either put the item back or put it in one of two piles: a throw-away pile (if it's in poor condition) or donate-to-charity pile (or potentially sell, although this delays the organization process). One rule of thumb is that if you've not used an item for a full year, chances are that you will not in the future.

- Create systems for closets, cupboards, and drawers. Folding clothing in thirds widthwise and then lengthwise allows you to stand the items up in a drawer or on a shelf so that all items can be seen with a quick glance. Arrange hanging clothes by type (dresses, pants/jeans, tops, sweaters, jackets) and by color. Only keep clothes that you love, that you actually wear, that fit, and that are in good condition. You might be surprised that you will not miss clothes you give away.

- Challenge yourself to remove enough items in those zones so that things are no longer cramped.

- Take advantage of organizing tools such as drawer dividers and baskets to harness like items.

- If you have children at home, let them be part of the organizational process, so that they can understand what goes where and can maintain the systems. The same is true for your spouse; involve him or her.

Organizing one area at a time makes the task less daunting, but I found I was so excited about how I felt with simpler, more organized areas that I kept going on to tackle other areas. In a few days I'd gone through every closet, cupboard, and drawer—taking literal carloads of items to the local charity thrift store, whose people loved seeing me walk in with items that would bless other people.

What areas of your home need to be organized?

Organize one of those spaces before your next First Place meeting and jot down how that made you feel here. Then share your success story with your group.

Lord God, You have given me so much. Thank you for being my abundance and blessing me!

[1] Stephanie Vozza, "*7 Ways Clutter Is Ruining Your Life.*" Fast Company, 9 Nov. 2015. https://www.fastcompany.com/3052894/7-ways-clutter-is-ruining-your-life#:~:-text=Americans%20collectively%20waste%209%20million,National%20Associa-tion%20of%20Professional%20Organizers.
[2] Kathi Lipp, "*How to Declutter Your Home Fast: 3 Clarifying Questions You Must Ask.*" Kathi Lipp, 21 May 2018. https://www.kathilipp.com/2018/05/how-to-declutter-your-home-fast-3-questions/

WEEK FIVE: FROM DISORDER TO DISCIPLINE

SCRIPTURE MEMORY VERSE
Now if you obey me fully and keep my covenant, then out of all nations you will be my treasured possession. Exodus 19:5

We all long to be dedicated people of faith, but often we have the perspective that this should happen spontaneously rather than with hard work. I want to be a person who has Bible verses at the ready, but I struggle with the daily practice of reviewing them so they shift from my short-term to long-term memory. I want to get rid of some weight around my middle, but I also have a weakness for simple carbs. I'd love to be physically stronger, but I rarely get out the weights.

The truth is that simple, daily disciplines probably will not kick into place without also putting spiritual disciplines into place. Daily I need a strong dose of God's Word to feed my soul. Daily I need refreshment that only comes from a devoted time of prayer.

It was no accident that the Israelites took a long rest stop at Mount Sinai. There Moses met the Lord on the mountain, where he received the Ten Commandments as well as other instruction for the people so that they would dedicate their hearts, minds, and souls to the Lord.

—— DAY 1: CAMPING OUT
Lord, I know that a life that is disciplined is a life that is aligned with Your Word. Show me how to abide with you.

At first glance camping out in the desert might seem like a not-so-pleasant experience. There are creepy crawly creatures, such as snakes and tarantulas that like to wander into your living spaces. And there are coyotes that bump and howl in the night. For my husband's and my first cross-country trip we camped in the Nevada desert the first night, and I remember very hurried trips to the restroom.

The third month after leaving Egypt, the Israelites camped at the foot of Mount Sinai (tradition says it's a mountain called Jebel Musa), which rises to 7,497 feet above sea level in a series of rugged mountains, many of which are higher. Today a small Bedouin population lives in that area—growing dates, barley, and some fruits—and raising camels, goats, donkeys, and sheep. The escaping Israelites may have found shelter there, as well as some mountain runoff for water.

They also found the Lord God and His direction for spiritual disciplines and boundaries for their lives.

Located in the south-central Sinai Peninsula, Mount Sinai, also known as Mount Horeb, is considered a sacred place in Israel's history where several biblical characters had significant encounters with the miraculous. Moses met God in the burning bush experience for his call to lead the Hebrews out of Egypt. The Lord made a covenant with his people Israel. And Elijah heard God in a gentle whisper. Sinai was a place of transition:

- For Moses from tending his father-in-law's sheep into a calling to lead the entire Hebrew nation out of Egypt.
- For the Hebrew people to transition into the nation Israel.
- For a transition from Elijah to Elisha as God's prophet.

When we camp out with God for an extended period of time, those seasons can be pivotal when we seek Him for new direction and disciplines.

Read Exodus 19:1-9. Where was God, whom did he call, and what was God's instruction (see v. 3)?

_____

_____

_____

Why do you think God mentioned what he did, as recorded in verse 4?

_____

_____

_____

In this next part of the passage, we find one of God's covenants with Israel. A covenant (*berit* in Hebrew) was a binding agreement between God and man. Here God pledges to be Israel's God as its Protector and the Guarantor of its blessed destiny.

The condition for Israel was the people had to agree to consecrate themselves to the Lord as His people—His kingdom—who would live by His rule and serve His purposes in history.[1]

Rephrase this covenant from verses 5 and 6 in your own words:

GOD'S AGREEMENT	ISRAEL'S CONDITION

How did the people respond when Moses told them what the Lord had said?

_____

_____

_____

Notice Moses's role here as an emissary between the Israelites and the Lord. God spoke to Moses. Moses relayed God's words to the people. When the people responded, Moses then took their answer back to the Lord. What are the two reasons the Lord said he would come to the people in a dense cloud (see v. 9)?

_____

_____

_____

The Israelites would have a challenging journey ahead. If they did not work together as one unified unit under the Lord's guidance, they would fail in their destiny to enter the Promised Land together. So God kept them camped out at Mount Sinai for about a year before they would move on. Here they would learn new disciplines for their lives: God's laws, rites for purification, and instructions for offerings and the observance of various holy days.

This may seem like a long time for training, but here are a couple of analogies to help our understanding. When an employee starts a new job, he goes through an orientation and perhaps a rigorous training period. A new cashier could not be expected or even trusted to handle a cash register without instruction. Similarly, when a young couple has their first baby, nurses carefully teach them about nursing, changing a diaper, cleaning the navel area, and even strapping the child correctly into a car seat. Those routines are not necessarily intuitive; training is imperative.

The same was true for the Israelites. They had been oppressed in Egypt and not been allowed to worship God publicly. Leaders had to be trained. The people had to be taught The Torah (the Law). Regulations had to be established in a routine fashion, so their new on-the-road nation could experience unity under God for their common mission: to travel as one to the Promised Land.

For what discipline deficit do you need to camp out with God right now? Complete this chart to guide you.

AREA OF STRUGGLE	WHAT DOESN'T SEEM TO BE WORKING FOR YOU IN EACH AREA?	HOW COULD GOD HELP YOU?
PHYSICALLY		
MENTALLY		
EMOTIONALLY		
SPIRITUALLY		

Father, I know You see these dysfunctions in my life. Help me see them clearly, but also help me see myself free of them as I seek a disciplined life.

—— DAY 2: UNDERSTANDING LIMITS

Lord, I need boundaries in my life—for my own benefit—but also so that my witness to others draws them to you as well. Help me choose them wisely.

The camping-out period at Mount Sinai was also a time for the Israelites to learn about the holiness of God. While they had witnessed a long series of the miraculous—from plagues to protection to provision—they needed instruction about how to conduct themselves before a holy God. The Lord told Moses,

> "I am the Lord your God; consecrate yourselves and be holy, because I am holy. Do not make yourselves unclean by any creature that moves about on the ground. I am the Lord who brought you up out of Egypt to be your God; therefore be holy, because I am holy." (Exodus 11:44-45)

Of course, holiness on our part is impossible. We are fallible, make mistakes, and sin. Thankfully, we learn from 1 John 2:2 that Jesus solved the sin problem for good by standing in our place before the Lord God, so that we can approach Him. Nonetheless, perhaps we need limits in our thinking and behavior so that others see God in us.

Read Exodus 19:10-25. What did the Lord tell Moses to tell the people to do (see vv. 10-11)? Why?

_____

_____

_____

What was a second instruction God told Moses to give (see v. 12)? If the people didn't obey this command, what would be the consequence?

_____

_____

_____

Just as the people were not to touch the tabernacle, they were also not to touch the mountain. The Lord's presence on the mountain made it holy, and that which is unholy cannot breach into that which is holy.

Review verses 16-19 and describe the scene of the morning of the third day for the meeting with God.

_____

_____

_____

We learn in Exodus 19:20 that the Lord called Moses to meet with him face to face at the top of the mountain. What was God's message to Moses (see v. 21-22)?

_____

_____

_____

Why was this teaching on the concepts of limits in regard to approaching God so important?

_____

_____

_____

Most of us never would have the opportunity to approach the President of the United States. However, if we knew someone close to him, we might be able to arrange a personal meeting. That person would serve as an intermediary to set up the meeting and introduce us personally. Without that connection, though, we would be standing outside the fence of the White House waving from a distance.

Every day we have the opportunity to approach God through prayer. We can approach His throne room of grace—not condemnation—because we have an advocate with the Father, Jesus, who serves as an intermediary or advocate.

If you had a Mount Sinai-type encounter with the Lord here on earth, how would you prepare for such a meeting? What new disciplines might you develop for yourself?

_____

_____

_____

Lord of Heaven and Earth, I understand that your Word says I am Your treasured possession, but I am far from being holy. Help me make choices that reflect Your holiness to the world around me.

—— DAY 3: REVERING GOD

Lord, you are holy and righteous and good. May I remember that and pause daily to give you the honor and praise due to you.

At the heart of any dysfunction or disorder in our lives may be a misunderstanding of or lack of regard for God. We may often forget that our greatest purpose is to love God and serve him forever.[2]

Probably the most renowned set of limits has been the Ten Commandments, given from God to Moses on Mount Sinai and then spoken to the Israelite nation awaiting at the foot of the mountain. Four of these ten establish a priority to revere God, and the remaining six establish laws governing people's behavior toward other people.

Read Exodus 20:1-11 and complete the following chart.

THE COMMANDMENT	SUMMARIZE IT IN YOUR OWN WORDS
FIRST COMMANDMENT (V. 3)	
SECOND COMMANDMENT (V. 4-6)	
THIRD COMMANDMENT (V. 7)	
FOURTH COMMANDMENT (V. 8-11)	

Yesterday we examined the Lord's characteristic of holiness. What do the first four commandments have to do with holiness?

Which, if any, of the commandments do you most struggle? How does that struggle relate to your physical, mental, emotional, and/or spiritual side?

Again, in Exodus 20:22-26 the Lord emphasizes to the Israelites that they should not make any gods. He also teaches them to make an altar for the purpose of bringing their sacrificial offerings to God, adding, "Wherever I cause my name to be honored, I will come to you and bless you" (Exodus 20:24). It was critical for the people to understand the Lord who had been and would continue guiding them was the one true God worthy of their reverent worship. Sacrifices would remind the people that it was the Lord alone Who should be honored.

We want hearts, minds, and souls that are dedicated to God. How could that type of devotion affect our physical well-being?

Write a prayer indicating Who the Lord God is to you personally.

Lord God, I lift Your name on high. You are the Lord of the universe—my Rock, my Redeemer, my Savior. I give all honor and glory and praise to You.

—— DAY 4: RESPECTING OTHERS

Lord, I recognize that loving You means that I also must love and respect others, because Your Son Jesus died for them too. Help me live out my faith.

While the first four of the Ten Commandments teach what it means to love and revere God, the last six address how we are to conduct our lives with one another. When an expert in the law asked Jesus which of the commandments was the greatest, Jesus said, "Love the Lord your God with all your heart and with all your soul and with all your mind. This is the first and greatest commandment." But he also added, "And the second is like it: 'Love your neighbor as yourself.' All the Law and the Prophets hang on these two commandments" (Matthew 22:37-40). Others have written that the two kinds of commandments can be summarized in two short statements. Love God. Love others. The apostle John wrote that our love for God is proven out through our love for others (1 John 4:7-8). And as lyricist John Mayer wrote, "Love Is a Verb." Our love for others is demonstrated, just as love for God is.

THE COMMANDMENT	SUMMARIZE IN YOUR OWN WORDS
FIFTH COMMANDMENT (V. 12)	
SIXTH COMMANDMENT (V. 13)	
SEVENTH COMMANDMENT (V. 14)	
EIGHTH COMMANDMENT (V. 15)	
NINTH COMMANDMENT (V. 16)	
TENTH COMMANDMENT (V. 17)	

What do the last six commandments have in common?

_____

_____

_____

Jesus summarized the teaching of the law and that of the prophets by saying, "Do to others what you would have them do to you" (Matthew 7:12). How does this require discipline on our part?

_____

_____

_____

How is obedience a spiritual discipline?

_____

_____

_____

Whom do you know in your First Place for Health group who needs some encouragement? How could you employ some love-is-a-verb steps to lift her or him this week?

_____

_____

_____

Father, I know that love is more than a feeling. It is kindness put in tangible form for others. It is a discipline of my mouth as well. Help me reflect You in the world around me.

—— DAY 5: PRACTICING DISCIPLINES
Lord, help me live out a devoted life by loving You and loving others.

After my mother retired from teaching elementary school, she started drafting house plans. She had been doing that as a favor for friends, but friends had friends who had friends...so it became a part-time business that eventually grew to more than two hundred clients. However, the year the state of California added more than three thousand new building codes, she called it quits. There simply was too much to remember, and after all, she was 81 years old.

Hearing of those new building codes, I remembered something my father said years before: "There should just be one law: be nice."

Unfortunately, "be nice" can be interpreted broadly, so God spelled out the law and regulations and requirements for annual observances and festivals. Most of the book of Leviticus is filled with those laws and regulations for worship for the Levites, as well as instructions on ceremonial cleanness, moral laws, holy days, the sabbath year, and the Year of Jubilee. The Israelites would simply not have under-stood "be nice to one another" or "be devoted to the Lord"; parameters had to be spelled out.

Numerous laws regarding justice and mercy are mentioned in Exodus 23. Read verses 1-9 and complete the following chart. The first one is done for you.

VERSE	SUMMARIZE WHAT IT SAYS	WHAT IS THE BROADER IMPLICATION?
v. 1	*Always do the right thing and tell the truth.*	*Don't allow others to pressure you to do what you know is wrong.*
vv. 2-3		
vv. 4-5		
vv. 6-7		
v. 8		
v. 9		

Now think of your health journey. List several principles you know are good for you and explain the rationale behind them. One example is given for you.

HEALTH PRINCIPLES	RATIONALE
Write down what you eat in a food tracker.	*This helps me recognize what I'm actually eating and not overeat.*

Often we might resist being told what to do. We'd like to be devoted to an exercise plan, but we probably don't prefer having a program dictated to us. We want to lose weight, but we still want to hang on to foods we think comfort us. We want to be devoted to the study of God's Word but allow other activities to take priority.

If your health or your spiritual life or day-to-day living is providing frustration or disappointment, something is not functioning well. In other words, the situation is dysfunctional. Abandoning dysfunctional practices to those that are disciplined can bring about dramatic changes. Ideas for making these shifts will be explored in the next two Reflection days.

You are God's treasured possession. You are worth the time it takes to make yourself more disciplined each day. Recite your scripture memory verse from this week, replacing the word *you* with your first name.

_____

_____

_____

Father, I recognize that something isn't working well in my life physically, mentally, emotionally, or spiritually, but I am ready to make changes for the better and trust You will guide me.

—— DAY 6: REFLECTION AND APPLICATION
Lord, teach me how to be more disciplined, so that I can make the most of my days and will effectively point others to Your kingdom.

Here are ideas to develop a disciplined life:

1. Start with basic spiritual disciplines—the daily study of God's Word and prayer. Those disciplines can occur early in the morning or late at night or another time during the day, but they are planned and faithfully followed. What will you do? _____

2. Ask God to reveal his purpose for your life. What are you sensing this is? _____

3. Define one SMART goal, which is as follows:
   Specific: a targeted area for improvement
   Measurable: quantified so you know when you've achieved it
   Achievable: possible to attain
   Relevant: makes sense, given the mission to which God has called you
   Time-bound: has a time-frame
   What is your SMART goal? _____

4. Visualize your achievement.
   What would reaching your goal look like? _____

5. Assess what might hold you back or distract you (such as junk food in the cupboards if you are determined to stay away from it).
   How could you be proactive here? _____

We are not alone in our personal walk of faith, just as the Israelites were not. We read this in Exodus 23:20-25:

> See, I am sending an angel ahead of you to guard you along the way and to bring you to the place I have prepared. Pay attention to him and listen to what he says. Do not rebel against him; he will not forgive your rebellion, since my Name is in him. If you listen carefully to what he says and do all that I say, I will be an enemy to your enemies and will oppose those who oppose you. My angel will go ahead of you and bring you into the land of the Amorites, Hittites, Perizzites, Canaanites, Hivites and Jebusites, and I will wipe them out. Do not bow down before their gods or worship them or follow their practices. You must demolish them and break their sacred stones to pieces. Worship the LORD your God, and his blessing will be on your food and water.

The Lord made several promises here to the Israelites, ones we can also hold close as we are journeying into a land of new discipline.

- God's presence will go with us.
- He will give us instruction if we pay attention.
- He will oppose our enemies if we do not rebel against Him.
- He will provide for and bless us as we worship only Him.

Lord God, thank You for your presence in this journey through life. May my worship and obedience bless You and draw others to your presence as well.

—— DAY 7: REFLECTION AND APPLICATION

Lord, I know that every day matters. Every day my choices can make a difference as to how I feel and how I can function in Your world.

Once we have established a big goal, then we can create actionable steps to build that new personal discipline into our lives. Here are additional steps that build on the Day 6 Reflection:

6. Make a plan. This new routine should be workable with your schedule and workable with your lifestyle.
    What steps do you need to take to reach your goal? _____
    _____
    _____
    _____

7. Just do it. We tend to argue or resist a new discipline at first. Develop the mindset that this is doable and the right thing to do. Ignore negative, I-don't-feel-like-it feelings.
    When will you start? _____

8. Record your baby step achievements.
    What are those? _____

9. Persevere. If you fail one day, just start again the next day. The only true failure is if you do not try.
    What will you tell yourself when you slip up? _____

10. Celebrate! Record your victories along the way.
    What's your first one? _____

The Israelites had a tough journey to move out of slavery into a Promised Land experience. The first generation on the road never crossed the finish line. They chose to fight God, complain, and disobey Him instead of trusting Him every step of the way. Their consequence was only seeing the Promised Land from a distance.

We are not promised an easy road for these travels. The Lord told the people there would be enemies ahead who would threaten them. Nonetheless, He said, "Little by little I will drive them out before you, until you have increased enough to take possession of the land" (Exodus 23:30). Simply because we have faith in God does not relieve us of this world's struggles. But we can know that He will establish our "borders" (Exodus 23:31) when we choose to follow Him and make the best choices for our lives. And those borders will be good for us.

[1] The *NIV Study Bible*. Ed. Kenneth Barker (Grand Rapids, Mich.: Zondervan Bible Publishers, 1985), 19.

[2] The Westminster Shorter Catechism, Purtian Reformed Theological Seminary. 20 April 2022. https://prts.edu/wp-content/uploads/2016/12/Shorter_Catechism.pdf

WEEK SIX: FROM INSECURITY TO IDENTITY

SCRIPTURE MEMORY VERSE
The Lord said to Moses, "Come up to me on the mountain and stay here."
Exodus 24:12

I sometimes joke that I grew up in a department store. My dad was the manager of large department stores in western U.S. states, but the most vivid memories I have come from an earlier position at Marsh's Department Store—a four-story building sandwiched between two others in the business district of a small city on the Hudson River in upstate New York.

I remember swishing through the revolving front doors of the store and feeling like the princess daughter of a king, with the sales ladies-in-waiting behind the glass counters smiling their hellos and escorting me to my dad. Their warm welcome was less about how they felt about me but more about their respect and admiration for my father, who treated his employees well and lived out the expression "The customer is always right."

Fast forward the years to my teens, when we lived in big cities in the West and when my identity shifted to how I felt about my appearance as someone who struggled with weight issues. I always felt less than others during those years until I came to a personal faith in Jesus Christ and finally began to see myself as loved and accepted by my heavenly Father.

When the Israelites took a year-long break at Mount Sinai, they finally had time to process who they were as God's chosen people, and God gave them the opportunity to enter into a lasting covenantal relationship with Him.

—— DAY 1: INVITED
Lord, sometimes I feel as though I never belong and loneliness sets in. Show me how I am invited to Your presence and into Your family.

The Hebrews' unifying identity in Egypt was less about their heritage of faith as ancestors of Abraham but more about their lives as slaves to Pharaoh. They were the outsiders after Joseph and his generation died. They were a problem to the new king, who said, "Look, the Israelites have become much too numerous for us. Come, we must deal shrewdly with them or they will become even more numerous and, if war breaks out, will join our enemies, fight against us and leave the country" (Exodus 1:9-10). The Israelites were not only the problematic outsiders; they were expendable.

When have you felt you didn't belong? What made you feel that way?

_____

_____

_____

Read Exodus 24:1-3. Who was invited to ascend the mountain to worship the Lord?

_____

_____

_____

Who could actually meet with the Lord? Why was that, do you think?

_____

_____

_____

Moses was the mediator between God and man. God spoke to him, and Moses spoke God's words to the people. Sometimes Jesus is referred to as the second Moses, but he was the mediator of a new covenant. Read Hebrews 3:1-6 and summarize what it says about Jesus.

_____

_____

_____

The difference between the mediation that occurred through Moses and that we experience now through Jesus is dramatic. Whereas only Moses could approach the Lord to speak with him, all those who now believe in Jesus Christ can approach God's heavenly throne room. In other words, you now are invited to the mountaintop. You are no longer an outsider in God's eyes. You now are included.

This concept may be foreign to you if you have never made a commitment to faith. If you would like to enter into a personal relationship with Jesus and become part of God's family, say this prayer aloud:

"Lord, I acknowledge that I have been living apart from You. I have done those things I should not have done, and I have left undone those things I should have. I understand this state of separation from You is called sin. I repent and ask Jesus Christ to come into my life to be my Savior and my Lord. Thank you, Lord, for hearing my prayer, in Jesus's name. Amen."

If you have prayed this prayer for the first time, how do you feel? If you made a commitment to Christ at some other time, when and where was that?

_____

_____

_____

Father God, thank You that You invite me into Your presence. It is a privilege I will not take lightly and that I will always treasure.

—— DAY 2: COVENANTED

Lord, I mess up a lot. Please show me that my relationship with You is binding and that You love me nonetheless.

When my husband Craig and I met with the minister who would perform our wedding ceremony, he challenged us to look at the traditional vows before we decided to write our own. When we did, we decided that "for richer or poorer, in sickness and in health" and the rest made a lot of sense. But Craig wanted one change—that we change the word *vow* to *covenant*. My now-rancher guy was in law school at the time, and he argued that people break vows all the time, but that a covenant was more than an agreement between us: it was also an agreement with the Lord.

While this study briefly examined the concept of covenant earlier, we will look at this in more depth now. The Bible Project explains the concept of covenant in simple terms:

> A covenant is a chosen relationship or partnership in which two parties make binding promises to each other and work together to reach a common goal. They're often accompanied by oaths, signs, and ceremonies. Covenants contain defined obligations and commitments, but differ from a contract in that they are relational and personal. Think of a marriage. In love, a husband and wife choose to enter into a formal relationship binding themselves to one another in lifelong faithfulness and devotion. They then work as partners to reach a common goal, like building a career or raising children together. That's a covenant.[1]

The concept of a *covenant* started with Adam and Eve in the Garden of Eden. While the word covenant was not explicitly used, God laid out the agreement that Adam and Eve would enjoy God's provision and blessings with one condition: they could not eat from the tree of knowledge and evil. Of course, they broke that covenant, and that brokenness changed humans' condition on earth for all eternity.

Read Exodus 24:3. When Moses came off the mountain, what did he do?

_____

_____

_____

How did the people respond?

_____

_____

_____

Then what three things did Moses do, as recorded in Exodus 24:4?

_____

_____

_____

During these times in the Near East there were three kinds of covenants:

- A royal grant: a covenant between a king and his people, usually perpetual and unconditional. God established several of these: with Abraham (Genesis 15:9-21), with Phinehas (Numbers 25:10-13), with David (2 Samuel 7:5-16), and with Israel (Jeremiah 31:31-34).

- A parity: A covenant between equals that bound them to friendship and mutual respect, such as found between Abraham and Abimelech (Genesis 21:27) and Solomon and Hiram (1 Kings 5:12).

- A suzerain-vassal: A covenant between a great king and one of his subject kings. The covenant on Sinai is an example, as was the agreement between the Lord and Abraham in Genesis 17.[2]

How was the covenant described in Exodus 24 a suzerain-vasssal covenant? What was that agreement?

_____

_____

Notice in Exodus 24:4 that after Moses wrote down everything the Lord had told him, he created a physical representation of the covenant between God and the twelve tribes of Israel. The altar was a visual reminder of God's presence, while the twelve stone pillars were a reminder that the people were in agreement with God.

The people responded to Moses by saying, "Everything the Lord has said we will do" (Exodus 24:3), then Moses wrote everything down. They would eventually leave Sinai for the Promised Land, so the altar at the foot of the mountain and the stone pillars would forever be left behind them. They needed God's words written down.

Write a covenant of your own. This can relate to your physical health or some other aspect of your well-being. It could also simply relate to your determination to live out your faith in obedience. You could incorporate scripture or simply write your own words, as you feel inspired. Share this with your First Place for Health group to solidify this commitment.

_____

_____

_____

Lord God, I choose Your lordship for my life. When there is a choice between fear and faith, I will choose faith. When there is a choice between doubt and trust, I will choose trust. I choose You.

—— DAY 3: COVERED
Lord, your love erases my sin, and I am thankful for your sacrifice.

There was another significant ritual that took place after the building of the altar and the stone pillars: the ratification of the covenant. Transactions and covenants in Old Testament times were ratified in one of several ways:

- Eating salt together for offerings (priests and Levites, Numbers 18:19).

- Eating a sacrificial meal (Jacob and Laban, Genesis 31:54).

- Passing between divided pieces of a slaughtered sacrifice (Abram and God, Genesis 15:17,17).

- Using blood.

Moses used the last of these. Read Exodus 24:4-8 and answer the following. What was done with the first half of the blood (see v. 6)? Then what was done with the rest?

Then what did Moses do with the first half of the blood (see v. 8)?

While these practices are gross by our standards today, they had significance then. The blood that was sprinkled on the altar represented God's acceptance of the earlier offering (see v. 5) as well as his forgiveness of the people. The sprinkling over the people represented the people's oath to follow through with their obedience to the covenant.

Jesus's institution of the Last Supper is a final symbolic and covenantal sacrament. Read the following scriptures:

> When Moses had proclaimed every command of the law to all the people, he took the blood of calves, together with water, scarlet wool and branches of hyssop, and sprinkled the scroll and all the people. He said, "This is the blood of the covenant, which God has commanded you to keep." In the same way, he sprinkled with the blood both the tabernacle and everything used in its ceremonies. In fact, the law requires that nearly everything be cleansed with blood, and without the shedding of blood there is no forgiveness. (Hebrews 9:19-22)

> Then he took a cup, and when he had given thanks, he gave it to them, saying, "Drink from it, all of you. This is my blood of the covenant, which is poured out for many for the forgiveness of sins. I tell you, I will not drink from this fruit of the vine from now on until that day when I drink it new with you in my Father's kingdom." (Matthew 26:27-29)

> In the same way, after the supper he took the cup, saying, "This cup is the new covenant in my blood, which is poured out for you." (Luke 22:20)

Jesus was the fulfillment of the promises of the Old Testament. His coming, death, and resurrection ended the need for the ritualistic practices the Jews performed for centuries. The "cleansing" using blood meant a cleansing from the darkness of sin. What replaced this practice? How do we remember his sacrifice today?

_____

_____

_____

We may feel bound by our past, which may have formed the identity that has seemingly held us down. Jesus was literally bound and crucified so that we do not have to live under those figurative bindings. Read what Anne Graham Lotz writes:

> Are you struggling with your bindings? Do you find that the more you fight against them, the ore pain you inflict on yourself, so that you are miserable in your confinement? Sometimes binding is in the will of God. Jesus was in the center of his Father's will, yet He was bound. He did not resist the tight cords or complain about His confinement. He simply submitted, not to the soldiers, but to His Father's will.[3]

The effect of Jesus's choice to be bound and crucified is our freedom from that which would bind us today.

The shedding of Jesus's blood covers our state of separation from the Father (Sin), as well as our mistakes and acts of disobedience (sins). Jesus has us covered in that regard, so that we are free from condemnation, guilt, and shame. How does knowing that free you to leave your past in the past and step confidently into the future? How does this affect your view of yourself?

_____

_____

_____

Father, I am so thankful that You sent Your Son Jesus so that my sins are covered forever. Help me live out my life in the knowledge of those mercies and Your amazing grace.

—— DAY 4: GUIDED
Lord, the world would direct me to paths that are not good for me. Guide my thinking, my emotions, my faith, and my health.

We have all kinds of questions on a daily basis. Should I go to college? Should I apply for a job? Should I marry this person? How should I advise my children? Should I attend this church or that one? Should I make a career switch...or push for an advancement...or move?

There is no shortage of sources to dish out all kinds of guidance: health experts and companies, the media and entertainment industry, social media influencers, and even GPS. But as we know, even GPS can send us in the wrong direction.

At the beginning of this study, we saw God call an insecure, unconfident, even resistant Moses who finally agreed to lead the Hebrews out of Egypt. He saw no inherent leadership abilities in himself, but he did eventually recognize that the Lord who called Himself I AM would tell him exactly what to do. Moses serves as a model for us as someone completely dependent on the Lord for guidance.

Read Exodus 24:9-18. Who went up the mountain and saw the God of Israel (see v. 9-10)?

_____

_____

_____

This was an important meeting for these leaders, most of whom earlier God said should not go up the mountain. We learn later in the Exodus story that they did not see God in the fullness of His glory—His face—because He told Moses, "no one may see me and live" (Exodus 33:20). But clearly, these elders, Moses, Aaron, and Aaron's sons Nadab and Abihu at least saw God's feet (Exodus 24:10). What did they see below them?

_____

_____

_____

The hike up the mountain could have taken two to three hours or more. What did they do on the mountain (see v. 11)?

_____

_____

_____

While the others returned back down the mountain, Moses remained there forty days. What was the purpose of this long visit with God (see v. 12)?

_____

_____

_____

Read Exodus 31:18. Who actually inscribed the tablets?

_____

_____

_____

Moses not only received the Ten Commandments, but also received instruction (in the next half dozen chapters of Exodus) about constructing the ark of the covenant, a wooden chest that would hold what was called the "Testimony"—the stone tablets with Ten Commandments, as well as instructions to make the following as well as those for observances and worship:

- Offerings

- The courtyard and curtained tabernacle, a portable sanctuary for a place of worship

- The altar

- Lamps, priestly garments, table

The Ten Commandments, as well as the other laws and instructions, would provide a tremendous means of guidance—the structure for the Israelites' society, for the worship of the Lord God, and for a means of judging disputes and crimes. Moses and the other leaders celebrated the sealing of the covenant with a covenantal meal, which foreshadowed the Lord's Supper.

What kind of guidance or direction do you need right now in your health journey or personal life?

_____

_____

_____

Try to take some time "up the mountain" in the next couple of days and just rest and wait there in that quiet place, seeking God's direction through prayer and His Word. Then record what you sense God is telling you to do.

Father God, You don't leave me flailing without a life compass. You are my Guide and knowing that helps me understand who I am: Yours.

—— DAY 5: WELCOMED
Father, Your welcoming me to dwell with You makes me feel loved and special. Thank You for continued reminders that You chose me.

I have a sign in my entry hall that reads, "Sit long. Talk much." There's nothing I enjoy more than having company in my home—friends and family for dinner and overnights. I have even started holding retreats in our home, which includes a guest house. My rancher husband and I also enjoy rich conversations, which deepen our relationships with others. I also love attending workshops and retreats sponsored by First Place for Health—mostly to connect with other like-minded friends of faith.

The Lord also invites us to dwell with him in His presence, to appreciate his glory (Exodus 24:17), and to hear from him. God told Moses, "Come up to me on the mountain and stay here..." (Exodus 24:12, emphasis added). Later the scriptures tell us, "And he stayed on the mountain forty days and forty nights" (v. 18, emphasis added). Our relationship with God is not meant to be a revolving door experience, where we zip into God's store, get what we want, and then zip out again. We are invited to stay, to dwell, to remain. The next chapters about setting up the tabernacle show the importance of creating not only physical room but also mental, emotional, and spiritual room for the presence of God in our lives.

Read Exodus 25:8. What was the purpose of the tabernacle?

_____

_____

_____

Read Exodus 29:45-46. What would the Israelites know as a result of the Lord's indwelling of the tabernacle, also called the Tent of Meeting?

Complete this fill-in-the-blanks exercise of those two verses.

"Then I will _____ among the Israelites and _____ their God. They will _____ that I am the Lord their God, who _____ them out of Egypt so that I might _____ among them. I am the Lord their God."

The people needed reminders of God's faithfulness, protection, and provision, as well as the fact that God was in their midst. They were not alone. They were called to be God's people. When they camped, the tabernacle would be a physical reminder that God was in the center of their camp and was meant to be at the center of their very lives.

How does knowing this affect how you perceive yourself? How does it form your own identity?

_____

_____

_____

On a regular basis we have the opportunity to remember God. Read Exodus 31:12-17. What is this observation and what is its purpose?

_____

_____

_____

Each week we are given a Sabbath. The day itself is holy, but it's also a day to remember the Lord makes us holy. On a continuous basis Jesus acts as our mediator. Hebrews 9:15-28 tells us Christ entered the Most Holy Place as a final offering once and for all, providing eternal redemption. The Father sees us as holy, welcomes us into an eternal relationship with Him, and invites us to stay with Him. Our worship and rest on the Sabbath are both for God and for us—so that we are reminded we are chosen and set apart for His work.

How do you observe the Sabbath (Sunday or another weekly day you choose)? How does this gift of a day from the Lord help you understand his love for you?

Lord God, You invite me to dwell with you. Remind me often that you accept me, welcome me, and love me.

—— DAY 6: REFLECTION AND APPLICATION
Father, You have not only welcomed me into your presence, but also sent Your Spirit to dwell within me. Remind me daily that my body is a tabernacle for the Living God.

For the Israelites the tabernacle was a physical representation and dwelling place for the Living God. Now there is another physical dwelling place for God's Spirit. First Corinthians 6:19 tell us the following:

> Do you not know that your body is a temple of the Holy Spirit, who is in you, who you have received from God? You are not your own; you were bought at a price. Therefore honor God with your body.

The Father welcomes us into His presence. Conversely, with our commitment to Christ, we have welcomed the presence of the God's Spirit in our lives. Jesus's holiness allows the Holy Spirit to dwell within us. How does knowing this affect how you perceive your tabernacle in these ways?

	If my body is the Spirit's tabernacle (dwelling place), I can honor him in these ways:
Physically	
Mentally	
Emotionally	
Spiritually	

Write this week's memory verse here:

_____

_____

_____

Imagine the greatest royalty on earth inviting you to visit and stay with him or her. Now remember that this is exactly what the King of Creation has already done for you. Often those who meet important figureheads have prepared questions. What questions do you have for the King of Creation?

_____

_____

_____

Lord God, help me to see myself just as You see me: chosen, holy, accepted, and welcomed. May I be mindful of that identity instead of the insecurities I've had in the past.

——— DAY 7: REFLECTION AND APPLICATION

Father, Your welcoming me to dwell with You makes me feel loved and special. Thank you for continued reminders that You chose me.

God's Word is full of affirmations about our identity. When we feel inadequate or down on ourselves, we can speak truth into our hearts and minds by repeating what the Bible says about us. Dr. Neil Anderson writes, "Understanding your identity in Christ is absolutely essential to your success at living the victorious Christian life!"[3]

Which of the following do you still need to claim for yourself?

_____ "Yet to all who did receive him, to those who believed in his name, he gave the right to become children of God." (John 1:12)

_____ "I no longer call you servants, because a servant does not know his master's business. Instead, I have called you friends, for everything that I learned from my Father I have made known to you." (John 15:15)

_____ "Therefore, there is no condemnation for those who are in Christ Jesus, because through Christ Jesus the law of the Spirit who gives life has set you free from the law of sin and death." (Romans 8:1-2)

_____ "Don't you know that you yourselves are God's temple and that God's Spirit dwells in your midst?" (1 Corinthians 3:16)

_____ "As God's fellow workers we urge you not to receive God's grace in vain." (2 Corinthians 6:1)

_____ "What agreement is there between the temple of god and idols? For we are the temple of the living God As God has said, 'I will live with them and walk among them, and I will be their God, and they will be my people.'" (2 Corinthians 6:16)

_____ "He predestined us for adoption to sonship through Jesus Christ, in accordance with his pleasure and will." (Ephesians 1:5)

____ "For we are God's handiwork, created in Christ Jesus to do good works, which God prepared in advance for us to do." (Ephesians 2:10)

____ "Being confident of this, that he who began a good work in you will carry it on to completion until the day of Christ Jesus." (Philippians 1:6)

____ "But our citizenship is in heaven. And we eagerly await a Savior from there, the Lord Jesus Christ." (Philippians 3:20)

____ "I can do all this through him who gives me strength." (Philippians 4:13)

____ "For he has rescued us from the dominion of darkness and brought us into the kingdom of the Son he loves, in whom we have redemption, the forgiveness of sins." ~Colossians 1:13-14

____ "And in Christ you have been brought to fullness. He is the head over every power and authority." (Colossians 2:10)

____ "For the Spirit God gave us does not make us timid, but gives us power, love and self-discipline." (2 Timothy 1:7)

____ "Let us then approach God's throne of grace with confidence, so that we may receive mercy and find grace to help us in our time of need." ~Hebrews 4:16

____ "The One who was born of God keeps them safe, and the evil one cannot harm them." (1 John 5:18)

How has your view of yourself changed since you made a commitment to follow Jesus Christ?

_____

_____

_____

Lord God, I lift Your name on high. You have done so much for me and continue to pour out Your mercies and Your grace. Help me move forward boldly to live my best life for Your sake.

[1] Whitney Woollard, "Covenants: The Backbone of the Bible: Partnerships between God and People," The Bible Project. 2018. https://bibleproject.com/blog/covenants-the-backbone-bible/?gclid=CjwKCAjwjtOTBhAvEiwASG4bCPOLjxZZukNMnQOj29_v2FwfW-taSzdDTkIbMF7F7ItV4XIOpg6K8HRoCn-IQAvD_BwE

[2] *"Major Covenants in the Old Testament," The NIV Study Bible.* Ed. Kenneth Barker. (Grand Rapids: Zondervan, 1985), 19.

[3] Anne Graham Lotz, *Just Give Me Jesus* (Nashville: Word/Thomas Nelson, 2000), 236.

[4] Neil Anderson, *"Who am I?"* pamphlet, Freedom in Christ.

WEEK SEVEN: FROM UNCERTAINTY TO CONFIDENCE

SCRIPTURE MEMORY VERSE
The Lord replied, "My Presence will go with you, and I will give you rest." Exodus 33:14

My daughter Rebekah's elementary school gave out character awards at the end of each school year: bravery, leadership, honesty, humility, loyalty, and so on. Each of the four years she attended that school, the staff gave her the Confidence Award. I think the staff forgot from year to year that they had given her that same award in the past, and she and I laugh about that today. To me that award epitomized my daughter's positive, indefatigable spirit. I always thought that no challenge fazed her, but she said recently, no, often she approached new and challenging tasks with a bit of uneasiness if not fear, but she simply trusted God for whatever He put in front of her.

I call that God-fidence: a full trust in the power, trustworthiness, and reliability in the Creator who made us and sustains us. There may be other forms of confidence:

- Self-confidence: The knowledge that one is trained and equipped to handle the tasks.
- Overconfidence: A misguided presumption of one's abilities.
- Arrogance: A sense of superiority over others.
- Illusion: An uninformed ignorance and carelessness of what a task involves, so that a person just forges ahead without a real sense of what to do.
- Optimism: A tendency to underestimate the difficulty of a challenge.
- Simulated confidence: A feigned display of confidence that masks what actually is a sense of inadequacy.[1]

The Israelites demonstrated some of these varied characteristics with the incident of the golden calf. From them we can learn how to break through from insecurity about ourselves and our abilities to a godly sense of confidence.

—— DAY 1: LEARN FROM MISTAKES
Father, I know You have been faithful in my past. Remind me of Your steadfastness as I face challenges ahead.

It's possible to mistake boldness or foolhardiness for confidence that comes from godly wisdom. We can begin to trust in our own common sense or advice from a crowd of influencers. Such was the case for the Israelites during the time Moses was on the mountain with God receiving the Ten Commandments and other instructions. From their mistakes we can learn and become more confident that our own decisions are wise.

Read Exodus 32:1-6. Why did the people meet up with Aaron to ask him to make gods (see v. 1)?

_____

_____

_____

What did Aaron tell the people to do (see v. 2)? And what did he do (see v. 3-4)?

_____

_____

_____

Refer back to Exodus 24:14. What two instructions had Moses told the elders before he went up the mountain to meet with God?

_____

_____

_____

Notice that in the narrative in Exodus 32, there seems to be no hesitation in Aaron about the people's request. Why do you think Aaron made such a seemingly confident yet drastically poor choice by making the golden calf?

_____

_____

_____

What other responses could Aaron have made to the Israelites' request?

_____

_____

_____

Recall a time when you made a drastically wrong decision. What consequences played out? What should you have done instead? What would you counsel someone else to do now in a similar situation?

_____

_____

_____

One way to build godly confidence in our lives is to not only read but study God's Word on a daily basis. Studying the Bible teaches us the difference between right and wrong, as well as the nature of God's character. We can learn from not only the right decisions that Bible characters made but also their mistakes, so that we can confidently make decisions in our own lives.

Do you view yourself as a confident person? Why or why not?

_____

_____

_____

Lord God, I pray that daily I become more confident in faith as I study Your Word and seek Your will for my life.

—— DAY 2: BE BOLD

Lord, thank You for building my confidence as I learn about You and grow in Your Spirit.

A long, prayerful history with God builds confidence. Early in this study (Exodus 3 and 4) we saw Moses's reticence to step into the role as the leader of the Exodus. He did not feel he had the credentials. He did not know what to say to the Israelites. He was afraid they would not believe that God had appeared or spoken to him. He felt he had no gift of speech, and then he simply stated he wanted the Lord to find someone else. We see a different Moses, however, when he came down from the mountain after meeting forty days with God.

Read Exodus 32:7-14. Why did the Lord tell Moses to go back down the mountain (see vv. 7-8)?

_____

_____

_____

MYplace O FOR BIBLE STUDY

What was the Lord's opinion of the people (see v. 9)? And what did He intend to do (see v. 10)?

_____

_____

_____

What are the elements of Moses's argument with the Lord (see vv. 11-13)?

_____

_____

_____

Why do you think Moses could so confidently approach the Lord Most High and make such an argument?

_____

_____

_____

How did the Lord respond (see v. 14)?

_____

_____

_____

We can confidently approach God today in prayer. Let's look at a couple teachings Jesus gave us about this subject in Luke 11:5-13:

> "Suppose one of you has a friend, and he goes to him at midnight and says, 'Friend, lend me three loaves of bread, because a friend of mine on a journey has come to me, and I have nothing to set before him.'

> "Then the one inside answers, 'Don't bother me. The door is already locked, and my children are with me in bed. I can't get up and give you anything.' I tell you, though he will not get up and give him the bread because he is his friend, yet because of the man's boldness he will get up and give him as much as he needs.

> "So I say to you: ask and it will be given to you; seek and you will find; knock and the door will be opened to you. For everyone who asks receives; he who seeks finds; and to him who knocks, the door will be opened.

"Which of you fathers, if your son asks for a fish, will give him a snake instead? Or if he asks for an egg, will give him a scorpion If you then, though, you are evil, know how to give good gifts to you children, how much more will your father in heaven give the Holy Spirit to those who ask him!"

Several principles about prayer come from this passage:

- We can pray confidently.

- We can pray boldly

- We can expect God to answer our prayers.

- The greatest answer to prayer is God's gift of Himself to us.

Think of a great need or desire you have right now and write a bold, confident prayer:

_____

_____

_____

Father God, thank You that we can approach you confidently, knowing that you care, you listen, and you will answer us.

—— DAY 3: DO THE NEXT RIGHT THING

Lord, I know that when I am not sure of all the details, I can simply do the next right thing.

You may know what it's like to go home from a special retreat or conference, only to find things are a mess at home—with all kinds of family issues and a mountain of laundry and dirty dishes. *So much for that mountaintop experience!* you might have thought.

The expression *mountaintop experience* comes from the Bible. Peter, James, and John saw the transfiguration of Christ on a high mountain (perhaps Mount Hermon just northeast of Caesarea Philippi, which today straddles the border between Lebanon and Syria just north of Israel). Then when Jesus and those disciples came down the mountain, they were immediately thrust back into the crowd with a man seeking mercy and healing for his demon-possessed son (Matthew 17:1-23).

The prophet Elijah had a mountaintop experience too. It was on top of Mount Carmel where God orchestrated victory for Elijah over 450 prophets of Baal (1 Kings 18:16-46). Then he sought refuge on Mount Horeb from Jezebel's hatchmen and God spoke to him not in wind, earthquake, or fire but in a gentle whisper (1 Kings 19:9-13).

The irony of a mountaintop experience is that right after we have had one of the most inspirational and spiritual times of our life, we often go home to face the valley struggles of not only daily life but perhaps even tougher news. That was true for Moses.

Read Exodus 32:15-35. What did Moses carry down the mountain (see vv. 14-16? Why were these objects special?

_____

_____

_____

How did Moses initially respond (see vv. 19-20)?

_____

_____

_____

Moses responded out of anger to the situation, showing that it's possible for even godly and confident leaders to let emotions dictate actions. After Moses' responses— which also included recruiting of the Levites to murder of three thousand people— Moses went back to the Lord.

Summarize what Moses said to the Lord (vv. 31-32).

_____

_____

_____

Now notice how the Lord answered him. Fill in the blanks for verses 33 and 34. "Whoever has sinned against me _____.

Now go, _____ to the place I spoke of, and _____ will go before you.

However, when the time comes for me to punish, _____."

And how did the Lord follow through (see v. 35)?

_____

_____

_____

While the Lord did not punish Moses for his anger-spurred reactions, it is apparent the Lord was not pleased with him for his actions. (It should be noted, however, that according to Exodus 34:1-4, Moses had to create the second set and lug them up the mountain, whereas God provided the original stone tablets.) When we aren't sure of the whole big picture, God simply wants us to do the next right thing. And often the next right thing is prayer. Moses skipped that layer with this incident.

When have emotions clouded your judgment and nudged you to make a response you have regretted? What should you have done instead?

_____

_____

_____

What is the fine line, do you think, between confidence and rashness? How could prayer make a difference between responding rashly and responding in a godly manner?

_____

_____

_____

Father God, develop confidence in me but not the kind that is clouded by my own pride and arrogance. I want You to be glorified in me.

——— DAY 4: MOVE ON
Lord, thank You that I need not dwell in my mistakes but that You help me pick up and move on.

The next chapter in Exodus shows us that we need not dwell in our sins and mistakes. The Lord provides clear directions for the Israelites to pick up and walk into the Promised Land.

Read Exodus 33:1-3. What is the good news for the Israelites? What is the bad news?

_____

_____

_____

Now read Exodus 33:4-6. Summarize what the Lord told Moses to say to the people.

_____

_____

_____

How did the people react (see v. 6)?

_____

_____

_____

Verse 4 may seem to conflict with verse 6, but it may be that some people already had ornaments on their clothing. The stripping away of ornaments of their clothing was a visual stripping away of their unmerited pride and sinfulness. Those ornaments would have been showy decorative items they would have attached to or layered on their clothing. Stripping them away demonstrated their regret, their repentance, their mourning for their decisions to disobey God, and their respect for the Lord, similar to how Jews used to tear their clothing or pile ashes on their heads. How would this have affected their confidence?

_____

_____

_____

If the Lord had chosen not to go with the Israelites, how could that have affected Moses, the leadership, and the people they were to lead to the Promised Land?

_____

_____

_____

How does repentance affect confidence? How could it lead to more confident behavior?

_____

_____

_____

Lord God, strip me of bad attitudes, ill motives, and arrogant behavior. May my confidence arise from a posture of humility and obedience.

—— DAY 5: FACE OFF

Lord, it simply astounds me that You invite me into your presence. Oh, may I do that continually all the rest of my days!

Moving forward confidently in our lives may be a matter of a faceoff. First, we would face God to know his will. Next we would face the facts of our situation and take them into consideration. And then we would face any fears and move through them to our own promised land. We see that when Moses takes a meeting with God in the Tent of Meeting.

Read Exodus 33:7-11. How did Moses facilitate this meeting with God (see v. 7)? What happened to announce this meeting (v. 9)? Who also was in this meeting (see v. 11)?

_____

_____

_____

How did the people react to what Moses did (see vv. 8, 10)?

_____

_____

_____

How did the Lord speak with Moses (see v. 11)?

_____

_____

_____

Read Exodus 34:33-35. What visual difference was there with Moses after having met with the Lord in the Tent of Meeting?

_____

_____

_____

Read Exodus 33:12-23. What did Moses need to know before leading the people into the Promised Land (see vv. 13, 15-16)?

_____

_____

_____

How did the Lord respond to Moses (see vv. 14, 17)? Why do you think the Lord changed his mind (refer to Exodus 33:3)?

_____

_____

_____

Read Exodus 33:18-23. Why do you think Moses asked the Lord to show him His glory?

_____

_____

_____

How could that have affected Moses's confidence that the Lord would, in fact, accompany them as they traveled into the Promised Land?

_____

_____

_____

Would a faceoff with God affect your trust in the Lord and your confidence in his plan for your life? Explain your answer.

_____

_____

_____

Moses desired to see God's glory, the fullness of God's very existence. Instead, the Lord said He would pass by, covering Moses with his hand until He had gone by him; only then did Moses see the Lord—but from behind not his face (Exodus 33:22-23). So a faceoff did not occur. But Jesus provided a different opportunity: he came to earth to display the fullness of God in the flesh. We can know God's goodness and character when we enter into a personal relationship with His Son. And someday we can experience the glory of the Lord when we pass into Heaven.

We can experience breakthrough and our God-fidence can soar when we rest on that assurance and seek Him in the pages of His Word and in prayer.

Holy God, I thank You that You made Yourself known through the person of Jesus Christ. May I be more like Him as I seek You each day.

—— DAY 6: REFLECTION AND APPLICATION
Lord, great is Your faithfulness! May I sing of Your love and goodness all of my days

A beautiful thing about scripture is that one book builds on another earlier book, just as verses and chapters develop ideas. Psalm 78 recounts God's history of faithfulness to the Israelites to remind them not to repeat the sins of the past and to keep faith in the Lord. Here are a few points the psalmist makes in verses 11 to 17:

> They forgot what he had done,
>> the wonders he had shown them.
> He did miracles in the sight of their ancestors
>> in the land of Egypt, in the region of Zoan.
> He divided the sea and led them through;
>> he made the water stand up like a wall.
> He guided them with the cloud by day
>> and with light from the fire all night.
> He split the rocks in the wilderness
>> and gave them water as abundant as the seas;
> he brought streams out of a rocky crag
>> and made water flow down like rivers.
> But they continued to sin against him,
>> rebelling in the wilderness against the Most High.

A recounting of God's history throughout their desert wanderings continues, showing God's faithful provision despite the Hebrews' complaints.

Then we read this in verses 38 and 39:

Yet he was merciful;
he forgave their iniquities
And did not destroy them.
Time after time he restrained his anger
And did not stir up his full wrath.
He remembered that they were but flesh,
A passing breeze that does not return.

Our confidence ultimately can be built on the assurance that despite our sin and mistakes, He is faithful to guide and protect us. Such confidence allows us to boldly step into His plan for our lives and escape the shadows of insecurity and even fear. Then we can experience the truth of this promise from Jeremiah 17:7: "Blessed is the one who trusts in the Lord, whose confidence is in him." We don't have to summon bravery or fortitude, because we can rest in the knowledge that God has been with us in the past, is with us now, and will carry us through whatever is ahead.

Write a psalm of your own, using the following prompts:

"Lord I have messed up so many times. Here are a few:

_____
_____
_____

"Yet you have been faithful, God, in these several ways:

_____
_____
_____

"So, God, I thank and praise You for

_____
_____
_____

Thank You, Lord God, for Your long history of care and provision in my life. May I be ever mindful of Your fingerprints all over my family and me.

—— DAY 7: REFLECTION AND APPLICATION
Lord, great is Your faithfulness! May I sing of Your love and goodness all of my days.

In her book *Becoming a Brave New Woman*, Pam Farrel writes,

> I like to say, "Show me your God, and I will show you your ability to achieve. Small God—small life. Big God—big opportunities and potential await. Big God equals big adventures. Big God leads to big bravery!" Too many of us, however, do not see God for who He really is. J.B. Phillips, in Your God Is Too Small, explains the quandary many of us find ourselves in:

> "We are modeling God upon what we know of man. That is why it is contended here that what at first sight appears to be almost a super adequate idea of God is, in reality, inadequate—it is based on too tiny a foundation. Man may be made in the image of God; but it is not sufficient to conceive God as nothing more than infinitely magnified man."[2]

Assuming your God is a big God, complete the following confidence-building, long-term plan. What one thing have you always wanted to do, but have put off for a long time?

_____

_____

_____

How might doing this help you grow physically, mentally, emotionally, and/or spiritually?

_____

_____

_____

What tasks would you need to do to complete your plan?

_____

_____

_____

What will you do first? And when will you do this?

_____

_____

_____

What structure will you create in your schedule so that you have time for this?

_____

_____

_____

When you begin struggling with this plan, what Bible verse will carry you through?

_____

_____

Create a prayer that you will pray as you carry this plan through.

_____

_____

_____

What fear will you set aside as you work through this plan?

_____

_____

When others criticize you for attempting this, what will you say?

_____

_____

How will you celebrate the milestones you make as you work through this plan?

_____

_____

Write this week's verse from memory:

_____

_____

_____

Lord God, it is a comfort to know that You go with me in my life's journey and lead me to a place of rest.

[1] John Spacey. "14 Types of Confidence." Simplicable, 20 May 2019. https://simplicable.com/new/confidence.

[2] Pam Farrel, *Becoming a Brave New Woman: Step into God's Adventure for You* (Eugene OR: Harvest House Publishers, 2009), 29. Quoted material: J. B. Phililips, *Your God Is Too Small* (New York: Collier, 1961), 42.

WEEK EIGHT: FROM CONFUSION TO CALLING

SCRIPTURE MEMORY VERSE
"The Lord himself goes before you and will be with you; he will never leave you nor forsake you. Do not be afraid; do not be discouraged." Deuteronomy 31:8

Have you ever turned God down? I did in my senior year of college. I had an application ready to send to an international campus ministries organization when all sorts of doubts began to plague me.

What would I have to offer?

Could I ever raise the needed funds?

Wasn't that "begging," as someone in my family had intimated?

Would God send me to someplace with no electricity where I couldn't speak the language?

So I pitched the application into the trashcan...and then lived with regret for the next thirteen years, knowing I had allowed unproven fears to cloud my judgment and sense of God's calling on my life. Finally, in my mid-30s I read a book called *"Lord, Change Me!"* by Evelyn Christenson that finally prompted me to submit my life to Christ's lordship and pray, "Use me, God." And that short prayer brought about several significant changes in my life.

Often people are confused about what they are supposed to do with their life. Perhaps this statement resonates with you. But we serve not a God of confusion but a God of clarity who makes our calling clear to us when we are open and willing. Breakthrough in this area of our lives gives us focused purpose for each of our days.

—— DAY 1: WILLING
Lord, You have a purpose and a plan for my life. May I be open and willing to Your calling.

Calling is a fascinating faith concept. While dictionaries might define the word as "a strong inner urge to follow a vocation," those of faith could define the word differently. God calls us to himself in relationship through His Son Jesus Christ. He wants to know us and for us to know Him, and He wants to provide an eternal relationship that will continue in Heaven, so that kind of call brings us in union with Him.

Here on earth we *call* one another on our cell phones, but God also might *call* us to prayer—to a time of reflection, communion, and communication. Again, there's the implication of God drawing us to Himself. I call this a "looking up" perspective.

In the Old Testament we read, "God called the light 'day,' and the darkness he called 'night' (Genesis 1:5)." Here He is naming things. Os Guinness said this type of calling is "far more than labeling, hanging a nametag on something to identify it." He said that kind of "decisive, creative naming is a form of making."

> Thus when God called Israel, he named and thereby constituted and created Israel his people. Calling is not only a matter of being and doing what we are but also of becoming what we are not yet but are called by God to be. Thus "name-calling," a very thing from name-calling, is the fusion of being and becoming.[1]

We *called* to Someone (God) to save us from our sins, but we are also called to something—to serve in a unique way that fulfills our life's purpose. God uses people to accomplish his will on this earth. And just as God called various people in the Bible to rise to certain callings, He can call us today to fulfill certain vocations.

Refer again to Exodus 3:7-10. What did God say to Moses (see v. 10)?

_____

_____

_____

Notice that it was God's idea to create a leader out of Moses, so he could lead the people out of slavery. Moses had stepped out of Pharaoh's life when he fled to Midian, but God had not lost track of him. Moses may have been leading a quiet life as a sheepherder, but God had other plans. Exodus 5:1 tells us that Moses and Aaron went to Pharaoh to request he let the Israelites go. Simple sheepherders undoubtedly could not have approached the supreme ruler of Egypt; perhaps only an adopted grandson could have: Moses.

So Moses led the people out of Egypt. But Moses would not be able to lead the people into Canaan, the Promised Land. Read Numbers 20:7-12. What did the Lord ask Moses to do (see v. 8)? What did Moses do (see v. 11)?

_____

_____

_____

Moses responded incorrectly to the Lord's instructions about getting water from the rock. This may seem like a little thing—simple forgetfulness or absentmindedness, perhaps. But the problem is that Moses wasn't listening correctly to the Lord. What were the consequences for Moses's behavior (see v. 12)?

_____

_____

_____

So the problem now exists that while Moses had led the people in the desert, he cannot be the one to lead the people into the Promised Land.

Read Numbers 27:12-14. What does God say will happen after Moses makes a trip up the mountain (see v. 13)?

_____

_____

_____

Mount Pisgah (commonly referred to as Mount Nebo) will provide Moses the viewpoint of the Promised Land, a place to which God will not allow him to enter. Years ago I chaperoned high school students for their final senior trip together to a well-known amusement park. Despite my counsel and warnings about trying to take illegal substances with them, one of my students got caught in a search at the gate and spent his day outside the park hanging out with the bus driver. His long-envisioned trip was never fulfilled. That student got left behind, as did Moses.

Listening to God is the first step in willingness to surrender our lives to Him. It is critical so we can first even hear God's calling in the first place. We need to be open and listening for his voice to begin with, so that we hear and know that call, but we also must listen to the step-by-step instruction that He may provide. Getting stuck on a Pisgah place in our lives is not a comfortable feeling. I lived in that limbo period for thirteen years. While I was working and raising our first three children and even serving in church ministry, I always knew something was missing in my life. And that void was of my own doing because I had not obeyed God's call in my 20s.

Recall a time when you knew God was calling you to some vocation. What was that? Did you follow through? Why or why not? And how did that pan out?

_____

_____

_____

Lord God, I submit myself to Your calling on my life. Use me. I will follow You and do whatever You want me to do.

—— DAY 2: GOD'S IDEA

Lord, Your ideas are best. May my will be bent to Yours as I attempt to follow Your call on my life.

There are several ways God can communicate a call to an individual. He can speak through His Word, through prayer, through circumstances, through other people, and even through dreams.

The first call on my life—to college campus ministry—I sensed directly through prayerful moments. I just knew God wanted me to serve and sensed that I could write for that organization's magazine and other publications. Years later when I met first one person and then another who worked in the publications office during that time period, it was the oddest of feelings: to think I could have known them for much longer, had I followed God's call.

Read Numbers 27:15-23. Who raised the question about the next leader of the Israelites (see vv. 15-17)?

_____

_____

_____

How did the Lord answer him (see v. 18)?

_____

_____

_____

What was Moses's part in this calling (see vv. 19-21)? What was he supposed to do?

_____

_____

_____

And how did Moses follow through (see vv. 22-23)?

_____

_____

_____

What specifically was Joshua to do?

_____

_____

_____

Notice that the call on Joshua was God's idea. Moses had the question, but God had the answer. Also notice that the text indicates Moses relayed God's call to Joshua (while it certainly is possible God also spoke directly to Joshua, but we don't know that), so there is the possibility that others can speak a call into our lives. Of course, we should always consider the validity and reliability of the communicating source. In Joshua's case Moses was a reliable, trustworthy conduit of God's call.

Joshua was also a logical candidate for this transition, as he was one of twelve spies who had scouted out Canaan for its military strength and farming potential. Only Joshua and Caleb provided positive reports about Canaan and provided leadership examples in affirming God's plan (see Numbers 13-14). They were the ones who provided this report (Numbers 14:7-9):

> "The land we passed through and explored is exceedingly good. If the Lord is pleased with us, he will lead us into that land, a land flowing with milk and money, and will give it to us. Only do not rebel against the Lord. And do not be afraid of the people of the land, because we will swallow them up. Their protection is gone, but the Lord is with us. Do not be afraid of them."

We don't hear the objections from Joshua that we heard from Moses. Joshua simply accepted the call to lead the entire Israelite community into the Promised Land.

Why is this, do you think?

_____

_____

_____

What call from the Lord have you sensed in your own life? How did you know? How did you respond? Write about this and share your story with your First Place for Health group.

_____

_____

_____

Lord God, You not only call me to be Your child but also serve You and Your people. Thank You for trusting me that much!

—— DAY 3: GET READY

Lord, I want to be sure I am hearing Your calling correctly. Please confirm that through Your Word, prayer, others, and/or circumstances.

Shortly after I prayed, "Lord, use me," I attended a women's retreat in the Sierras near Lake Tahoe. It was there while sitting on a rock and praying that I sensed God saying, "I want you to write for me." Frankly, I had no idea what that might involve. I had a journalism degree and had worked for a daily newspaper, but I knew nothing about freelance writing for Christian publications. Shortly thereafter, though, I learned of a Christian writers' conference, and my husband encouraged me to go. There I began to understand how God could use my writing...and here I am several decades later writing this Bible study.

Simply because God calls us to a specific ministry or vocation does not necessarily mean that the road ahead will be easy. The call may not sync with our own goals or plans and may not necessarily sync with our current skills or education. A call is not an easy road, but the fact that God has called you means He trusts you and He will equip you for whatever is ahead.

Even after Moses commissioned Joshua to lead the Israelites, Joshua was still in training. The Lord continued to speak to the people through Moses His additional instructions in regard to offerings that were to be part of their regular worship. Once the people would spread throughout Canaan, their disbursed nature could have caused them to forget those worship practices.

We read of those instructions in Numbers 28-29 for daily offerings as well as those for Sabbath and monthly offerings and offerings for the Passover, the Festival of Harvest, the Festival of Trumpets, the Day of Atonement, the Festival of Shelters. Laws concerning vows between a husband and wife as well as between a father and a young daughter follow in Numbers 30.

Moses was also still the leader for the conquest of the Midianites (Numbers 31), a nomadic group that was near the Promised Land when the Israelites arrived. Despite the fact that Moses married a Midianite woman, the Israelities and the Midianites had always been bitter enemies.[2] The Midianites had a sinful lifestyle that would draw the Israelites away from the Lord. Joshua must have been involved in military leadership, but we don't read of his overall leadership yet. Despite the fact that Joshua was called to lead, he had not yet been officially commissioned. He was still in training.

Read the following verses and complete the chart, indicating some of what Moses continued to teach the Israelites (including Joshua) through three different addresses before they cross over the Jordan River into the Promised Land. (The first one is done for you.) While just a single verse reference is given for you, I encourage you to read the context of that verse and then write any other verse that stood out to you.

Deuteronomy reference	What was the overall teaching?	Another verse I found helpful
Moses's First Address: Ch. 1-4:43	Moses reminded the Israelites of how the Lord had led the people for the last 40 years.	Deut. 4:30: "Return to the Lord your God and listen to what he tells you."
Moses's Second Address: Ch. 5:1		
Moses's Third Address: Ch. 29:9		

Moses's book-length instructions reminded the people of the Lord's faithfulness, the laws and regulations the Lord had given them, and the importance to follow and obey the Lord once they entered the Promised Land.

After receiving God's call to write for Him, I attended three week-long writers' conferences that first year. I also sought the counsel of experienced writers and editors as I started writing articles and devotions and learned the value of constructive criticism. Mostly, I learned that I had a lot to learn; I still sit under others' instruction more than three decades later.

As you consider a calling you sense the Lord has on your life, what kind of training or counsel would you need to fulfill that call? How might you pursue that?

_____

_____

_____

Father, thank You for entrusting me with Your kingdom work. May I pursue my calling with diligence and passion.

—— DAY 4: BE STRONG
Lord, I see that a calling on my life can provide many challenges. This will not be easy but I trust You to provide everything I need.

A second call on my life came in a most peculiar way just three years after the call to write: a literal nightmare. In my dream I was on a chartered bus along with City of Sacramento officials (I used to live in that area) who were showing off a new public housing area that had been constructed from a former slum. As we drove toward that district near the downtown, I could see beautiful new homes in an area near the American River. While children were waving from porches, windows, and even rooftops, they were unaware that their homes were all on fire. The children would die if someone didn't do something.

I tried to call others' attention to the potential disaster, but no one would pay attention to me. So I ran to the front of the bus and screamed to the driver, "Stop the bus! I have to get off!"

Then I awoke, knowing God was calling me to be a teacher. Such an experience is not so crazy as it may seem. Joseph of the Old Testament had life-changing dreams, as did Joseph of the New Testament. Their dreams actually saved lives.

Teaching also can save—or at least positively direct—young people's lives. For many years others had told me I would be a great teacher, but I always dismissed their comments, because that was one of two professions I never wanted to pursue (the other was nursing). I knew in my gut, though, that the call was unmistakable and within a month I had enrolled in a graduate program to pursue teaching credentials. A year later I was teaching high school English—something I never thought I would enjoy doing, but later I found I loved the challenge of teaching and advising young people.

It is true that some simply know their life's calling and pursue it from their youth. But others—like me—may need a divine revelation or figurative whack on the head. I never wanted to teach, because my mother had been a teacher, because I knew it would be hard, and because I wanted to forge my own path. But clearly, teaching is in our family blood, as both my daughters also are English teachers. I've had several occupations so far in my lifetime (also newspaper journalist, technical writer/editor, law office administrator and paralegal), but teaching was definitely the hardest.

The Lord laid out to Moses challenges Joshua would face. Read the following scriptures in Deuteronomy and write what those challenges ahead.

Reference	What challenge lay ahead?	How would God help Joshua?
Deut. 31:3		
Deut. 31:5		
Deut. 31:7		
Deut. 31:16		
Deut. 31:17-18		
Deut. 31:21		
Deut. 31:29		

Read Deuteronomy 34:9. Joshua had difficult tasks ahead of him, but what do we learn about him and his effectiveness as a leader?

_____

_____

_____

What do you think are the most important characteristics needed for the calling you sense God has on your life? Or if you're not certain of your calling, what are the most important characteristics for a Christian leader (perhaps even your First Place for Health leader)?

_____

_____

_____

What growth areas are you sensing need to be developed in your own life to fulfill a calling?

Physically: _____

Mentally: _____

Emotionally: _____

Spiritually: _____

Father, I have a long way to go. Help me make better choices this week so that I am worthy of Your calling.

—— DAY 5: THE ONE

Lord God, it is a humbling moment when I realize You have chosen me to serve in Your behalf. Equip me, Father.

More than eight years after the call to teach, God had something more for me to do. Again, that particular calling on my life came in a most peculiar way. I had been falling apart physically. I was overweight. I got out of breath going up stairs. And I needed painkillers to sleep at night, because of pain in my hips. The worst moment was when I walked out my back door one day and found myself in a crumpled heap because my knee had given way. I knew I needed to do something about my health, but I also knew God had been asking me to spend more time with him.

As I pushed myself off the pavement I decided things would change. I would get up a little earlier the next morning and go walking. And while I walked. I would pray. There was a lot of "myness" in my prayers: my marriage, my kids,, my job as a teacher. But that all changed one day when I saw what I call a single daddy's ballet.

Before six in the morning, I watched a young man I knew park his pickup truck in front of Toddler Towers in my little town in the Sierras, go around to the other side, and swoop up the cutest little toddler girl. As he handed that blanketed babe to the daycare worker on the sidewalk, the little one said, "Bye, Daddy. Love you."

I knew right then that God had me walking the streets of my community less for the myness of my prayers but more for the needs of others. So I prayed for that young man as he headed an hour off to Reno. Then I opened my eyes to my community and saw with fresh eyes the needs of the business owners, the folks in homes, the loggers headed into the woods, the millworkers headed to the mill. And I prayed for them.

My prayer life dramatically changed as I discovered everywhere I go, there is a need for prayer. I just needed to open my eyes...and my heart.[3] I also experienced dramatic changes. I lost two dress sizes. The depression that had clouded most of my adult life vanished, and I was no longer plagued by irrational fears and anxiety. Pursuing a calling I thought would change others and my community also changed me.

Following a calling is life changing. Read Joshua 1:1-18. What was Joshua's initial challenge (see v. 2)?

_____
_____
_____

What was the Lord's assurance (see v. 3-5)?

_____
_____
_____

What were the specific instructions the Lord gave Joshua (see vv. 6-9)?

_____
_____
_____

Notice here that for the first recorded time the Lord was now speaking directly to Joshua. What did the Lord say twice to Joshua (see vv. 6, 9, 18)? Why thrice, do you think?

_____

_____

_____

What would be the scariest part of a call on your life? What would assure you as you pursued this calling?

_____

_____

_____

Fill in the blank of Joshua 1:6:
"Be strong and courageous, for you are _____ _____ who will lead these people to possess all the land I swore to their ancestors."

The Lord told Joshua he was "the one." This commentary helps us understand why.

> Joshua succeeded Moses as Israel's leader. What qualifications did he have to become the leader of a nation? (1) God appointed him (Num. 27:18-23). (2) He was one of only two adults who had witnessed the Egyptian plagues and the exodus from Egypt. (3) He was Moses' personal aide for 40 years. (4) Of the 12 scouts, only he and Caleb showed complete confidence that God would help them conquer the land.[4]

But why wasn't Caleb "the one"? When ten of the twelve spies gave negative scouting reports about the "giants" in Canaan, it was Caleb who said, "We should go up and take possession of the land, for we can certainly do it" (Numbers 13:30). But God is sovereign; only He knows who is the best one for a certain calling. And it's interesting to note that after the people crossed the Jordan River, Caleb advocated for the hill country God had promised him (Joshua 14:6-15), whereas the Israelites gave land to Joshua (Joshua 19:49-51). Perhaps there was a difference of character God considered between the two strong and courageous men.

We may have the tendency to think someone else might be better for the calling. Or we might even believe we don't have the time or simply not want to take on that responsibility. We may have not the slightest interest in that vocation or ministry, but that interest and even passion for it could very well develop after we pursue what God has asked us to do. A calling is different than a simple job or assignment. Remember, it's God's idea...and when something is God's idea, it's better than our own perception.

Write out this week's memory verse, Deuteronomy 31:8. Then make it your prayer.

_____

_____

_____

Father, You are not the author of confusion. You see what is best, and You call those You love for certain jobs. I pray I am worthy of whatever You have for me.

—— DAY 6: REFLECTION AND APPLICATION

Lord God, You called creation into being. You formed and knew me before I was born. I offer up all that I am to You for your earthly plan.

The oldest psalm in the book of Psalms, Psalm 90, actually was written by Moses. Read it here:

> Lord, you have been our dwelling place
>   throughout all generations.
> Before the mountains were born
>   or you brought forth the whole world,
>   from everlasting to everlasting you are God.
> You turn people back to dust,
>   saying, "Return to dust, you mortals."
> A thousand years in your sight
>   are like a day that has just gone by,
>   or like a watch in the night.
> Yet you sweep people away in the sleep of death—
>   they are like the new grass of the morning:
> In the morning it springs up new,
>   but by evening it is dry and withered.
> We are consumed by your anger
>   and terrified by your indignation.
> You have set our iniquities before you,
>   our secret sins in the light of your presence.

All our days pass away under your wrath;
    we finish our years with a moan.
Our days may come to seventy years,
    or eighty, if our strength endures;
yet the best of them are but trouble and sorrow,
    for they quickly pass, and we fly away.
If only we knew the power of your anger!
    Your wrath is as great as the fear that is your due.
Teach us to number our days,
    that we may gain a heart of wisdom.
Relent, LORD! How long will it be?
    Have compassion on your servants.
Satisfy us in the morning with your unfailing love,
    that we may sing for joy and be glad all our days.
Make us glad for as many days as you have afflicted us,
    for as many years as we have seen trouble.
May your deeds be shown to your servants,
    your splendor to their children.
May the favor of the Lord our God rest on us;
    establish the work of our hands for us—
    yes, establish the work of our hands.

Moses was born into slavery and should not have survived infancy. Pharaoh had ordered all male babies be killed to decrease the threat to his power, as the Israelites grew in number under his reign. Instead, Pharaoh's own daughter rescued baby Moses from the river, where his mother was hiding him in a basket, and he was raised in Pharaoh's own home. When Moses ran away to escape punishment for killing an Egyptian for beating a Hebrew, Moses may have thought his influence was out of the picture. However, God chose him to lead the Hebrew nation out of slavery.

What circumstances in your life might convince you that you are not as qualified as someone else for a calling or vocation?

Now "flip" those. How might those very disadvantages give you a better perspective and perhaps even an advantage over others?

Close in prayer today by thanking God for the challenging circumstances and disadvantages of your life, as you offer them and yourself up to God.

Lord God, here I am. Use me. Send me. Allow me to serve You in ways that are beyond my abilities, so that You alone are glorified.

—— DAY 7: REFLECTION AND APPLICATION

Lord God, allow Your Word to speak truth into my life. Cancel the confusion and clarify the calling.

As I have shared, I have followed three callings (besides a call to raise our four children, of course) on my life: to write, to teach, and to pray. Each has had its challenges, but each has given me a sense of purpose, joy, and fulfillment. A call need not be something scary or outside our natural interests, giftings, and skills. Those also could nudge us toward a calling.

One way to gain clarity about calling or even simple next steps of direction is to read God's Word. How do the following verses provide direction and even assurance about calling?

"I have come that they may have life, and have it to the full." (John 10:10b)

"'For I know the plans I have for you,' declares the Lord, 'plans to prosper you and not to harm you, plans to give you hope and a future.'" (Jeremiah 29:11)

_____

_____

_____

"For we are God's handiwork, created in Christ Jesus to do good works, which God prepared in advance for us to do." (Ephesians 2:10)

_____

_____

_____

"Now to him who is able to do immeasurably more than all we ask or imagine, according to his power that is at work within us, to him be glory in the church and in Christ Jesus throughout all generations, for ever and ever! Amen." (Ephesians 3:20)

_____

_____

_____

"It is God who works in you in order to fulfill his good purpose." (Philippians 2:13)

_____

_____

_____

"And we know that in all things God works for the good of those who love him, who have been called according to his purpose. For those God foreknew he also pre-destined to be conformed to the image of his Son, that he might be the firstborn among many brothers and sisters." (Romans 8:28-29)

_____

_____

_____

How might you confidently step into a calling on your life...or renew your enthusiasm for one of which you are already aware?

_____

_____

_____

What next steps might you take in that direction?

_____

_____

_____

Lord God, You have called me for Your purpose, and that purpose is good—not only for Your kingdom's sake but also for mine. I trust You for all the details ahead.

[1] Os Guinness, "What Is a Calling?" Cru. 2010. https://www.cru.org/us/en/blog/leadership/what-is-a-calling.html.

[2] *Chronological Life Application Study Bible* (Carol Stream, IL: Tyndale House, 2005), 277.

[3] More information about prayerwalking can be found in this resource: Janet Holm McHenry, *PrayerWalk: Becoming a Woman of Prayer, Strength and Discipline* (Colorado Springs: WaterBrook/Penguin Random House, 2010).

[4] *Chronological Life Application Study Bible*, 336

WEEK NINE: A TIME TO CELEBRATE

To help you shape your short victory celebration testimony, work through the following questions in your prayer journal, one on each day leading up to your group's celebration.

DAY ONE: List some of the benefits you have gained by allowing the Lord to transform your life through this First Place for Health session. Be mindful that He has been active in all four aspects of your being, so list benefits you have received in the physical, mental, emotional and spiritual realms.

DAY TWO: In what ways have you most significantly changed mentally? Have you seen a shift in the ways you think about yourself, food, your relationships, or God? How has Scripture memory been a part of these shifts?

DAY THREE: In what ways have you most significantly changed emotionally? Have you begun to identify how your feelings influence your relationship to food and exercise? What are you doing to stay aware of your emotions, both positive and negative?

DAY FOUR: In what ways have you most significantly changed spiritually? How has your relationship with God deepened? How has drawing closer to Him made a difference in the other three areas of your life?

DAY FIVE: In what ways have you most significantly changed physically? Have you met or exceeded your weight/measurement goals? How has your health improved during the past twelve weeks?

DAY SIX: Was there one person in your First Place for Health group who was particularly encouraging to you? How did their kindness make a difference in your First Place for Health journey?

DAY SEVEN: Summarize the previous six questions into a one-page testimony, or "faith story," to share at your group's victory celebration.

May our Mighty God make you victorious in Him, as you continue to keep Him first in all things!

LEADER DISCUSSION GUIDE

For in-depth information, guidance and helpful tips about leading a successful First Place for Health group, spend time studying the *My Place for Leadership* book. In it, you will find valuable answers to most of your questions, as well as personal insights from many First Place for Health group leaders.

For the group meetings in this session, be sure to read and consider each week's discussion topics several days before the meeting—some questions and activities require supplies and/or planning to complete. Also, if you are leading a large group, plan to break into smaller groups for discussion and then come together as a large group to share your answers and responses. Make sure to appoint a capable leader for each small group so that discussions stay focused and on track (and be sure each group records their answers!).

—— WEEK ONE: FROM BONDAGE TO BREAKTHROUGH

1. Sometimes we don't face the fact that we are in bondage to a bad habit. Why is that, do you think?
2. In Day 1 you were asked to write down an internal issue with which you struggle. Be brave and share that with our group.
3. In Day 2 you listed some excuses for not moving forward with a struggle. Be brave again and share those with the group, so that we can support one another.
4. In Exodus 4:18-20 Moses takes a couple first steps. What were those and why do you think he did those things?
5. What might be first steps toward breakthrough in your journey
6. Day 4 refers to Pharaoh's answer of "tomorrow." What "tomorrow" thing that you have been procrastinating will you begin today?
7. What was the impetus in Exodus 12:24-51 that caused Pharaoh to boot the Hebrews out of Egypt (Day 5)?
8. Sometimes it takes a negative health experience for us to make big changes in our lives. That could be a bad health report or aching joints. What has caused your breakthrough in attitude to make you take on a healthier plan?
9. What do you find inspirational from Jeanne Donovan's story in Day 6?
10. Which one or more of Dr. Phil's questions strike you?

—— WEEK TWO: FROM CHALLENGE TO GOD'S CONTROL

1. Sometimes we face unexpected health or other challenges that seemingly throw off our health routines. How have you found success to stay on course during such a season?

2. Day 1 discusses the Israelites detour in Exodus 13:17-22. Why did God not lead the Israelites directly through the Philistine country?

3. What detour have you recently experienced? What possible benefit could there have been for that?

4. Day 2 addresses the moments the Israelites got directed toward the Red Sea with the Egyptian army on their heels. What did they learn from that experience, do you think?

5. Have you had a "stand still" moment in your life—a time when you felt you were simply to wait for God to work out the details? Share that with the group.

6. God parted the waters for the Israelites. When has God come through with a major breakthrough for you that seemed miraculous?

7. What are some principles about facing your fears that you learned from Day 3?

8. Day 4 is about celebrating the wins in our lives. What are some healthy ways to celebrate a weight loss or exercise win?

9. Even after the Red Sea miracle, the Israelites soon turned to complaints when they had no water. What will you do this next week to sustain you through desert times?

10. Share a helpful idea you got from Days 6 or 7.

—— WEEK THREE: FROM HURTS TO HEALING

1. Refer to the Numbers 12:1-16 story about Miriam, Aaron, and Moses and discuss what you think each person's viewpoint might have been.

2. How should we respond when we are attacked unfairly?

3. How did some review of Miriam's and Moses's history provide some context in Day 2?

4. There is certainly a difference between excuses and reasons for someone's behavior. Discuss this with the group.

5. Perhaps you would like to share how someone hurt you, but how you sought to understand any underlying reasons. How did that situation resolve or how might you pray for resolution?

6. Day 3 asks you to speculate how relationships break down. Would anyone like to share their answer?

7. From Day 4 explain what triggers tend to create conflicts in your home?

8. What purpose does forgiveness play in restoring relationships?
9. How do we forgive someone when there is no recognition of wrongdoing from that other person?
10. What did you find from Day 7 that was helpful in regard to forgivenesss that could help bring about breakthrough in emotional healing?

—— WEEK FOUR: FROM OVERWHELMED TO ORGANIZED

1. How do you struggle with organization of your home or schedule?
2. Review the Exodus 18 story. What was the problem Jethro had noticed?
3. How did that issue arise, do you think?
4. What plan did Moses's father-in-law suggest? And how did Moses respond?
5. Do you have a problem delegating responsibilities? Why or why not?
6. What responsibilities could you realistically let go?
7. Day 5 refers to a wise practice of setting limits. What kinds of limits or boundaries would help you?
8. What kind of organizational help do you need? What would help you maintain good health and other routines?
9. What principles about God's provision resonated with you in Day 6?
10. What tips from Day 7 could help you get organized?

—— WEEK FIVE: FROM DISORDER TO DISCIPLINE

1. What do you consider spiritual disciplines and which ones do you practice?
2. If you could "camp out" with God in a spiritual retreat, what kind of help would you hope to receive (see Day 1)?
3. Day 2 speaks of the importance of holiness. How is holiness related to the concept of boundaries?
4. If you could have a Mount Sinai-type encounter with God, how would you prepare for such a meeting?
5. Day 3 reviews the first four of the Ten Commandments. How would you summarize all of them in one statement?
6. What do you think it means to be devoted to the Lord?
7. Day 4 discusses the last six of the Ten Commandments. How would you sum those up in one statement?
8. If it's true that love is a verb, how do we live that out?
9. What health principles did you list in Day 5? Which ones do you follow?
10. Share your thoughts from Days 6 and 7 about making goals and plans.

—— WEEK SIX: FROM INSECURITY TO IDENTITY

1. Tell the group what it means to you to be God's chosen.
2. In what circumstances have you not felt included?
3. Day 1 provides an opportunity for you to ask Jesus into your life. If you have prayed that prayer, share with the group about when that occurred and how it made you feel.
4. What were the three kinds of covenants as mentioned in Day 2?
5. What was the covenant the Israelites made in Exodus 24?
6. The Last Supper and communion were mentioned in Day 3 in relationship to the Old Testament sacrifices. What does communion mean to you as a point of identity?
7. In Day 4 we were reminded that God guided the Israelites. How does knowing God help you make daily decisions?
8. In Day 5 we learned that the tabernacle was placed in the center of the Hebrews' camp as a physical reminder that God was in their midst—that they were His. What reminds you continually of God's presence in your life?
9. We learned in Day 6 that our bodies are now the tabernacle of the living Spirit of God. How does knowing this influence how you might perceive and treat your body.

—— WEEK SEVEN: FROM UNCERTAINTY TO CONFIDENCE

1. In what areas are you confident? In what areas are you not?
2. How could mistakes we've made actually make us more confident in the future?
3. Day 2 discusses Moses's relationship with God. How has Moses grown as a character from the time when God first called him?
4. What are several principles about prayer that we learn in Day 2?
5. What is the difference between confidence and rashness, do you think (see Day 3)?
6. How does repentance affect confidence (see Day 4)? How could it lead to more confident behavior?
7. Explain the faceoff concept introduced in Day 5.
8. Would a faceoff with God affect your trust in Him? Explain your answer.
9. Share the psalm you may have written for Day 6.
10. Share the plan you explained in Day 7

—— WEEK EIGHT: FROM CONFUSION TO CALLING

1. Have you sensed a calling from God on your life? Share that with the group.
2. Day 1 discusses the concept of willingness in relationship to calling. Why is this important?
3. Day 2 discusses the fact that the call on Joshua's life was God's idea, even though Moses brought up the subject of who would lead the Israelites into the Promised Land. Why is this important?
4. What were some of the reminders Moses gave the Israelites in his three addresses to the people (see Day 3)?
5. How should someone follow through with a calling from God?
6. Joshua did not have an easy road, as we learn in Day 4. What were some of those?
7. What do we learn about Joshua's effectiveness as a leader from Deuteronomy 34:9?
8. What are some of the most important characteristics needed for someone God has called to leadership?
9. What special lines spoke to you in Day 6 in Psalm 90?
10. Which verse in Day 7 particularly struck you? Why?

—— WEEK NINE: TIME TO CELEBRATE

As your class members reflect on each week's content, help them remember the ways strength has risen because of following Christ fully in each area of life. Ask: What have you learned in this study that has made you stronger?

FIRST PLACE FOR HEALTH
JUMP START MENUS

All recipe and menu nutritional information was determined using the Master-Cook software, a program that accesses a database containing more than 6,000 food items prepared using the United States Department of Agriculture (USDA) publications and information from food manufacturers.

As with any nutritional program, MasterCook calculates the nutritional values of the recipes based on ingredients. Nutrition may vary due to how the food is prepared, where the food comes from, soil content, season, ripeness, processing and method of preparation. You are expected to add snacks and sides as needed to meet your nutritional needs. For these reasons, please use the recipes and menu plans as approximate guides. As always, consult your physician and/or a registered dietitian before starting a weight-loss program.

Breakfast Pizza

1 whole-wheat naan
2 tablespoons part-skim ricotta cheese
1 tablespoon marinara (can use pesto)
½ teaspoon lemon zest
1 large egg
1 tablespoon grated Parmesan cheese
Chopped fresh basil and ground pepper for garnish

Preheat oven to 425°F. Coat a baking sheet with cooking spray. Place naan on prepared pan. Mix ricotta, marinara (or pesto) and lemon zest in a small bowl. Spread the mixture onto the naan, creating a well in the center. Carefully crack egg into the well. Sprinkle with Parmesan. Bake until the naan is golden, the egg white is set and the cheese is melted, 8 to 10 minutes. Garnish with basil and pepper, if desired. Serves 2

Nutritional Information (1/2 Pizza): 225 calories, 8g fat, 101g cholesterol, 370mg sodium, 25g carbohydrates, 2g fiber, 12g protein

Live It Tracker: 2 oz-eq. grain, ½ oz protein

Cauliflower Tacos with Avocado Cream

large head of cauliflower, cut into small florets
2 tbsp taco seasoning (see below)
2 tbsp olive oil
2 tbsp lime juice (1 lime)
8 Corn tortillas
cilantro
shredded cabbage
Avocado Cream
1 avocado
1 garlic clove, minced
1/2 cup light sour cream
1/2 tsp salt
1/4 cup lime juice
1/4 cup cilantro

Preheat oven to 400°F. In a large bowl toss cauliflower with taco seasoning, olive oil and lime juice then spread on a large baking sheet. Place on center rack and roast for 30 minutes or until cauliflower is tender. While cauliflower is roasting prepare avocado cream by placing all ingredients in a food processor or small blender and blending until smooth. Warm tortillas and add roasted cauliflower along with shredded cabbage and fresh cilantro. Top with avocado cream and serve. Serves 4

Taco Seasoning

1 tablespoon chili powder	½ teaspoon paprika
¼ teaspoon garlic powder	1 ½ teaspoons ground cumin
¼ teaspoon onion powder	1 teaspoon salt
¼ teaspoon crushed red pepper flakes	1 teaspoon black pepper
¼ teaspoon dried oregano	

Add all to bowl and mix well. Store for up to 3 months in container with tightly-fitting lid.

Nutritional Information: 185 Calories, 11g Fat, 4g Protein, 21g Carbohydrate, 3g Fiber, 2mg Cholesterol, 247mg Sodium

Live It Tracker: 1 oz-eq grain

Easy Black Bean Soup

1 Tbsp oil
1 cup diced white onion
3 cloves garlic, minced
¼ tsp each sea salt & black pepper
2 15-ounce cans black beans, drained
2 cups broth
2 tsp ground cumin
1 ½ tsp chili powder
¼ tsp ground coriander
1-2 chipotle peppers in adobo sauce, optional
3 Tbsp cocoa

Heat a large pot over medium heat. Add oil onion and garlic. Season with salt and pepper and sauté for 4-5 minutes. Add black beans, broth, cumin, chili powder, coriander, chipotle peppers and dark chocolate. Bring to a simmer over medium heat and reduce heat to low. Cook uncovered for about 20 minutes. Serves 6

Nutritional Information: 317 Calories, 5g Fat, 17g Protein, 54g Carbohydrate, 13g Fiber, 1mg Cholesterol, 646mg Sodium.

Live It Tracker: 2 oz Protein OR ½ cup vegetable

Apple Cinnamon Oatmeal

    4 crisp apples, divided
    1 cup steel-cut oats
    4 cups water
    3 tablespoons packed brown sugar, divided
    ½ teaspoon ground cinnamon
    ¼ teaspoon salt
    ½ cup nonfat plain Greek yogurt

Shred 2 apples using the large holes of a box grater, leaving the core behind. Heat a large saucepan over medium-high heat. Add oats and cook, stirring, until lightly toasted, about 2 minutes. Add water and the shredded apples; bring to a boil. Reduce heat to maintain a simmer and cook, stirring frequently, for 10 minutes. Meanwhile, chop the remaining 2 apples. After the oats have cooked for 10 minutes, stir in the chopped apples, 2 tablespoons brown sugar, cinnamon and salt; continue cooking, stirring occasionally, until the apples are tender and the oatmeal is quite thick, 15 to 20 minutes more. Divide the oatmeal among 4 bowls. Top each portion with 2 tablespoons yogurt and 3/4 teaspoon brown sugar.

Nutritional Information (about 1 ¼ cup): 282 Calories, 8g Protein, 59g carbohydrates, 6g fiber, 2g fat, 166mg sodium

Live It Tracker: 2 oz-eq grain, 1 cup fruit

Chopped Cobb Salad

2 cups fat-free, low-sodium chicken broth
3 cups chopped iceberg lettuce
1 cup roasted chicken
1 stalk celery, diced
1 carrot, diced
1 hard-boiled egg, diced
1 tablespoon crumbled blue cheese
2 tablespoons honey-mustard vinaigrette (see below)

Arrange lettuce, chicken, celery, carrot, egg and blue cheese in a salad bowl or sealable container. Before serving, drizzle with dressing. Serves 1

Nutritional Information: 481 calories, 17g protein, 67g carbohydrate, 13g fiber, 4g fat, 282mg sodium

Live It Tracker: 3 oz protein, 1 ½ cup vegetable

Honey Mustard Vinaigrette
1 clove garlic, minced
1 tablespoon white-wine vinegar
1 ½ teaspoons Dijon mustard
½ teaspoon honey
⅛ teaspoon salt
Freshly ground pepper, to taste
1/3 cup extra-virgin olive oil

Whisk garlic, vinegar, mustard, honey, salt and pepper in a small bowl. Slowly whisk in oil. Store in container with tightly-fitted lid.

Easy Enchilada Bake

1 cup shredded zucchini
1 tablespoon finely chopped sweet red pepper
1 teaspoon olive oil
1 garlic clove, minced
3/4 cup frozen corn
3/4 cup black beans, rinsed and drained
1/8 teaspoon salt
1/8 teaspoon ground cumin
3/4 cup salsa
2 tablespoons minced fresh cilantro
3 corn tortillas (6 inches)
3/4 cup shredded low fat cheddar cheese
Sour cream, optional

Preheat oven to 350°. In a large skillet, sauté zucchini and pepper in oil until pepper is crisp-tender. Add garlic; cook 1 minute longer. Add the corn, beans, salt and cumin; sauté 2-3 minutes longer. Stir in salsa and cilantro. Place a tortilla in the bottom of a 1-1/2-qt. round baking dish coated with cooking spray. Spread with 2/3 cup vegetable mixture; sprinkle with 1/4 cup cheese. Repeat layers twice. Bake, uncovered, until heated through and cheese is melted, 20-25 minutes. Let stand 10 minutes before serving. If desired, serve with sour cream. Serves 3

Nutritional Information: 286 calories, 11g fat, 30mg cholesterol, 676mg sodium, 37g carbohydrate, 5g fiber, 12g protein.

Live It Tracker: 3 oz-eq grain, 1 ½ cup vegetable

Blueberry Oatmeal Cakes

2 ½ cups old-fashioned rolled oats
1 ½ cups low-fat milk
1 large egg, lightly beaten
⅓ cup pure maple syrup
2 tablespoons canola oil
1 teaspoon vanilla extract
1 teaspoon ground cinnamon
1 teaspoon baking powder
¼ teaspoon salt
¾ cup blueberries, fresh or frozen

up to 12 hours. Preheat oven to 375 degrees F. Coat a 12-cup nonstick muffin tin with cooking spray. Stir egg, maple syrup, oil, vanilla, cinnamon, baking powder and salt into the soaked oats until well combined. Divide the mixture among the muffin cups (about 1/4 cup each). Top each with 1 tablespoon blueberries. Bake the oatmeal cakes until they spring back when touched, 25 to 30 minutes. Let cool for 10 minutes. Serve warm.

*Freeze for up to 3 months

Nutritional Information (2 cakes): 264 calories, 7.4g protein, 40g carbohydrates, 4g fiber, 8g fat, 34mg cholesterol, 210mg sodium

Live It Tracker: 2 oz-eq grain

Tuna Pita Wraps

4 small pitas
2 (4.5 ounce) cans tuna
Mediterranean Salad (recipe below)
Tzatziki (recipe below)
1 (15 ounce) can chickpeas, drained and rinsed
1/4 cup chopped Kalamata olives
Green leaf lettuce

Mediterranean Salad

1 cucumber, peeled and seeds removed, finely diced
2 plum tomatoes, peeled and seeds removed, finely diced
1 tablespoon extra virgin olive oil
1 tablespoon fresh lemon juice
2 tablespoon chopped parsley
Kosher salt
Freshly ground black pepper

Tzatziki

1 cup plain nonfat Greek yogurt
1/2 cucumber, peeled
1 lemon, juiced
1 clove garlic, minced
2 tablespoons finely chopped fresh mint
1/4 teaspoon dried oregano
Kosher salt

Place tuna, Mediterranean salad, tzatziki, chickpeas, olives, and lettuce on pita.

Mediterranean Salad

Combine all ingredients in a small mixing bowl and season with Kosher salt and freshly ground black pepper.

Tzatziki

Using the small grate of grater, grate cucumber. Soak excess cucumber moisture with paper towels. In a small mixing bowl, combine Greek yogurt, 3 tablespoons of the grated cucumber, two tablespoons lemon juice, garlic, mint, and dried oregano. Season with Kosher salt.

Nutritional Information: 328 calories, 9g fat, 21g protein, 41g carbohydrates, 3g fibber, 17mg cholesterol, 756 sodium

Live It Tracker: 2 oz-eq grain, 2 oz protein, ½ cup vegetable

5-minute Tacos

4 eggs
½ tablespoon chili powder
½ tablespoon garlic powder
½ tablespoon cumin
¼ teaspoon kosher salt
½ tablespoon olive oil
4 taco sized tortillas or 8 mini tortillas
Purchased salsa fresca or pico de gallo
1 handful thinly sliced red onion
Torn cilantro leaves
Hot sauce

In a medium bowl, whisk together the 4 eggs. Add the chili powder, garlic powder, cumin, and kosher salt, and whisk until combined. In a skillet, heat the olive oil. Add the eggs and cook over medium low heat, scraping as the eggs solidify, about 3 to 4 minutes total. As you scrape, they'll start to form together into a meat-like texture. Don't scrape too much or you'll make too small of pieces: just enough for that it comes together! If time, warm and char the tortillas by placing them on an open gas flame on medium for a few seconds per side, flipping with tongs, until they are slightly blackened and warm. (See How to Warm Tortillas.)

Top with salsa fresca (drain extra liquid before serving), thin sliced red onions, torn cilantro leaves, and hot sauce. Serves 2

Nutritional Information: 316 calories, 15g fat, 29g carbohydrates, 4g fiber, 16g protein

Live It Tracker: 1 oz-eq grain, 2 oz protein

Breakfast Tostada

¼ cup black beans, rinsed
2 tablespoons water
2 tablespoons lime juice, divided
¼ teaspoon taco seasoning
¼ avocado, mashed
¼ cup diced Roma tomato
1 tablespoon diced white onion
Pinch of salt
1 (6-inch) corn tortilla
Nonstick cooking spray
1 large egg
¼ cup shredded romaine lettuce

Combine black beans, water, 1 tablespoon lime juice and taco seasoning in a microwave-safe bowl. Microwave on High for 2 minutes. Using a fork, mash the beans into a paste; set aside. Mash avocado with a fork in a small bowl. Add tomato, onion, the remaining 1 tablespoon lime juice and a pinch of salt. Set aside. Coat tortilla on both sides with cooking spray. Heat a small nonstick skillet over medium heat. Add the tortilla to the pan and toast, flipping once, until crisp and lightly browned on both sides, 3 to 4 minutes. Transfer to a plate. Crack egg into the pan and reduce heat to medium-low. Cook, flipping once if desired, until the white is set, 2 to 3 minutes. To assemble the tostada, layer the bean mixture, avocado mixture and lettuce on the tortilla. Top with the egg.

Nutritional Information: 365 calories, 15g protein, 40g carbohydrates, 11g fiber, 19g fat, 186mg cholesterol, 600mg sodium

Live It Tracker: 1 oz-eq grain, 1/2 cup vegetable

Mediterranean Chickpea Salad

1 (15-oz.) can chickpeas, drained and rinsed
1 medium cucumber, chopped
1 bell pepper, chopped
1/2 red onion, thinly sliced
1/2 c. chopped kalamata olives
1/2 c. crumbled feta
Kosher salt
Freshly ground black pepper
Lemon Parsley Vinaigrette
1/2 c. extra-virgin olive oil
1/4 c. white wine vinegar
1 tbsp. lemon juice
1 tbsp. freshly chopped parsley
1/4 tsp. red pepper flakes
Kosher salt
Freshly ground black pepper

Make salad: In a large bowl, toss chickpeas, cucumber, bell pepper, red onion, olives, and feta. Season with salt and pepper. Make vinaigrette: In a jar with a tight-fitting lid, combine olive oil, vinegar, lemon juice, parsley, and red pepper flakes. Shake until well mixed. Add dressing to salad just before serving. Serves 6

Nutritional Information: 359 Calories, 25g Fat, 9g Protein,26g Carbohydrate, 7g Dietary Fiber, 11mg Cholesterol, 307mg Sodium

Live It Tracker: 1 cup vegetable, 1 tsp oil

Pork Chops with Nectarines

2 teaspoons chili powder
1 teaspoon ground coriander
1/2 teaspoon ground cumin
1/2 teaspoon paprika
1/4 teaspoon salt
1/4 teaspoon pepper
4 boneless pork loin chops (4 ounces each and 1/2 inch thick)
1 tablespoon olive oil
1/4 cup salsa
2 tablespoons apricot spreadable fruit
2 cups sliced peeled nectarines or peaches
2 tablespoons minced fresh cilantro
1 teaspoon dried oregano

In a small bowl, combine the first 6 ingredients. Rub on both sides of pork chops. In large nonstick skillet, cook pork chops in oil over medium-high heat until juices run clear, 5-6 minutes on each side. Remove to a platter and keep warm. In the same skillet, combine salsa and spreadable fruit. Bring to a boil. Reduce heat and cook, stirring, over medium heat for 1 minute. Stir in nectarines, cilantro and oregano; cook until heated through, 2-3 minutes. Serve with pork. Serves 4

Nutrition Information: 246 calories, 10g fat, 55mg cholesterol, 279mg sodium, 15g carbohydrate, 2g fiber, 23g protein.

Live It Tracker: 3 oz protein, ½ cup fruit

Fruit Bar

1 cup chopped nuts, divided
¾ cup whole-wheat pastry flour
¾ cup all-purpose flour
½ cup sugar
½ teaspoon salt
4 tablespoons cold unsalted butter, cut into small pieces
1 large egg
2 tablespoons canola oil
1 teaspoon vanilla extract
¼ teaspoon almond extract

Fruit Filling
3 ¼ cups diced mixed soft dried fruit (about 16 ounces), divided
1 ½ cups apple cider
½ cup sugar
¼ cup cornstarch
1 teaspoon vanilla extract

To prepare crust: Combine 3/4 cup oats, whole-wheat flour, all-purpose flour, sugar and salt. Cut in butter until well incorporated (can use food processor for these steps. Whisk egg, oil, 1 teaspoon vanilla and almond extract in a small bowl. Add to oats mixture and combine until it starts to clump (will be crumbly). Measure 1/2 cup of the mixture and combine in a bowl with the remaining 1/4 cup oats. Set aside for the topping. Preheat oven to 400 degrees F. Coat a 9-by-13-inch baking dish well with cooking spray. To prepare fruit filling & assemble bars: Combine 2 cups dried fruit, cider, sugar and corn-starch in a large saucepan. Bring to a simmer over medium heat, stirring constantly, until the mixture is very thick, 4 to 5 minutes. Stir in the remaining 1 1/4 cups dried fruit and 1 teaspoon vanilla. Transfer the dough to the prepared baking dish. Spread evenly and press firmly into the bottom to form a crust. Spread the fruit filling over the crust. Sprinkle the reserved topping over the filling. Bake the bars for 15 minutes. Reduce oven temperature to 350 degrees and bake until the crust and topping are lightly brown, 25 to 30 minutes more. Let cool completely before cutting into bars.

Nutritional Information (1 bar): 243 calories, 3g protein, 40mg carbohydrates, 3g fiber, 8g fat, 17mg cholesterol, 240mg sodium

Live It Tracker: 1oz-eq grain, ½ cup fruit

Spicy Salmon Bowl

Salmon

1/3 c. low-sodium soy sauce
1/4 c. extra-virgin olive oil
1/4 c. chili garlic sauce
Juice of 1 lime
2 tbsp. honey
4 cloves garlic, minced
4 (4-oz.) salmon fillets

Spicy Mayo

1/2 cup light mayonnaise
2 tbsp. Sriracha
2 tsp. toasted sesame oil

Quick Pickled Cucumbers

1/2 c. rice vinegar
1 tbsp. granulated sugar
1 tsp. kosher salt
2 tsp. toasted sesame oil
3 cucumbers, thinly sliced

Bowls

Cooked brown rice
1 avocado, sliced
1 medium carrot, grated
1/2 red onion, thinly sliced
Cilantro leaves, torn

Make salmon: Preheat oven to 350° and line a large baking sheet with foil. In a medium bowl, whisk together soy sauce, olive oil, chili garlic sauce, lime juice, honey, and garlic. Add salmon and gently toss to combine. Place on prepared baking sheet and bake until salmon is fork-tender, 20 to 25 minutes. Meanwhile, make pickled cucumbers: In a microwave-safe bowl or jar, add vinegar, sugar, and salt and microwave until sugar and salt are dissolved, about 2 minutes. Stir in sesame oil, then add cucumbers and shake to combine. Cover with a tight-fitting lid or plastic wrap until ready to use. Make spicy mayo: In a small bowl, combine mayonnaise, Sriracha, and sesame oil. Assemble bowls: Divide ½ cup rice among 4 bowls. Top with salmon, pickled cucumbers, avocado, carrot, red onion, cilantro, and sesame seeds. Drizzle with spicy mayo. Serves 4

Nutritional Information: 467 Calories, 27g Fat, 22g Protein, 39g Carbohydrate, 5g Fiber, 55mg Cholesterol;, 1494mg Sodium

Live It Tracker: 2 ½ oz protein, 1 cup vegetables, 1 tsp oil

Spicy Chicken Bowl with Tangy Slaw

1 tsp. sweet paprika
1/2 tsp. ground cumin
1/2 tsp. ground cinnamon
1/4 tsp. salt
1/4 tsp. Pepper
4 (5-ounce) boneless skinless chicken breasts
1 tbsp. olive oil

Tomato Salad

1 pt. cherry tomatoes, halved
1 tbsp. olive oil
1 sliced scallion
Pinch salt
Pinch Pepper

Sweet and Tangy Slaw

2 tbsp. cider vinegar
1 tbsp. honey
1/4 tsp. salt
1/4 tsp. Pepper
1/2 large head red cabbage, cored and shredded

Make chicken: Combine sweet paprika, ground cumin, cinnamon, salt, pepper, and pinch of red pepper flakes. Rub onto chicken breasts. Heat olive oil in a large skillet on medium. Cook chicken breasts until golden brown, 2 to 3 minutes per side. Transfer to oven and roast at 425°F until just cooked through, 9 to 11 minutes. Make tomato salad: Toss cherry tomatoes with olive oil, scallion, salt, and pepper. Make slaw: Whisk together cider vinegar, honey, salt, and pepper. Toss with red cabbage. Let sit, tossing occasionally, at least 10 minutes or refrigerate up to 3 days. Assemble bowls: Combine arugula, chicken, tomato salad, and slaw in bowl.
Serves 4

Nutritional Information: 325 calories; 10g protein; 42g carbohydrates; 3g fiber; 25g fat 53mg cholesterol 63mg; 738mg sodium

Live It Tracker: 4 oz protein, 1 cup vegetable

Breakfast Tostada

2 (6 inch) corn tortillas
½ cup canned black beans, rinsed and drained
2 eggs
1 tablespoon fat-free milk
⅛ teaspoon black pepper
Dash salt
Nonstick cooking spray
½ cup chopped tomato
2 tablespoons shredded Monterey Jack cheese
2 teaspoons fresh cilantro
1 ounce chunky salsa

Warm tortillas according to package directions. Meanwhile, in a small bowl use a potato masher or fork to slightly mash beans; set aside. In another small bowl or 1-cup glass measure combine eggs, milk, pepper and salt. Beat with a wire whisk or rotary beater. Lightly coat an unheated medium nonstick skillet with nonstick cooking spray. Preheat over medium heat then pour egg mixture into hot skillet. Cook, without stirring, until egg mixture begins to set. Run a spatula around edge of skillet, lifting egg mixture so that the uncooked portion flows underneath. Continue cooking about 2 minutes more or until egg mixture is cooked through but is still glossy and moist. Remove from heat. Spread tortillas with mashed beans. Divide cooked egg mixture between tortillas. Top with tomato, cheese, and cilantro. If desired, top with salsa. Serve immediately. Serves 2

Nutritional Information (1 tostada): 215 calories, 15g protein, 24 carbohydrates, 5g fiber, 8g fat, 219mg cholesterol, 409mg sodium

Live It Tracker: 1 1/2 oz. protein, 1 oz-eq grain

Deli-Style Hoagie

1 16 ounce loaf French bread
4 ounces light dairy sour cream ranch dip
1 cup shredded lettuce
¾ cup shredded carrot (1 large)
8 ounces thinly sliced cooked roast beef, ham, or turkey
½ of a medium cucumber, seeded and shredded
4 ounces thinly sliced provolone cheese

Cut French bread in half horizontally. Spread dip on cut sides of bread. On the bottom half of the bread, layer lettuce, carrot, roast beef, cucumber, and cheese. Top with top half of bread. Cut sandwich into 8 portions. Secure portions with decorative toothpicks. Makes 8 servings.

Nutritional Information: 239 Calories, 10g Fat, 6g Protein; 32g Carbohydrate 2g Fiber, 3mg Cholesterol, 518mg Sodium

Live It Tracker: 2 oz-eq grain, ½ cup vegetable

Sheet Pan Chicken with Asparagus

3 tbsp. all-purpose flour
kosher salt
4 boneless, skinless chicken breasts
2 tbsp. olive oil
1 small red onion
1 clove garlic
1 ½ cups low-sodium chicken broth
1 lb. asparagus
1 c. frozen edamame
2 tbsp. chopped fresh dill
1 tbsp. sour cream
1 tbsp. fresh lemon juice

In a shallow bowl, whisk together the flour and 1/2 teaspoon each salt and pepper. Coat the chicken breasts in the flour mixture. Heat the oil in a large skillet over medium-high heat and cook the chicken breasts until golden brown on one side, 4 to 6 minutes. Turn the chicken, add the onion and garlic and cook, stirring the onion and garlic occasionally, for 3 minutes. Add ½ cup broth to the skillet and simmer, scraping bottom, until reduced by half, 1 to 2 minutes. Add the remaining broth, return to a boil, then reduce the heat and simmer until the chicken is cooked through, 5 to 6 minutes more. Two minutes before the chicken is done, add the asparagus and edamame to the skillet and cook, stirring occasionally, until just tender.

Remove from heat and stir in dill, sour cream, and lemon juice. Serve with potatoes or crusty bread, if desired. Serves 4

Nutritional Information: 426 Calories; 15g Fat, 58g Protein, 12g Carbohydrate, 2g Fiber, 146mg Cholesterol, 141mg Sodium

Live It Tracker: 4 oz protein, 1 cup vegetable

Chewy Granola Bars

1 cup low-fat granola
1 cup rolled oats
½ cup mixed nuts
½ cup whole-wheat flour
⅓ cup raisins, dried cherries, dried cranberries, and/or snipped dried apricots
1 egg, beaten
3 tablespoons packed brown sugar
3 tablespoons oil
3 tablespoons honey
½ teaspoon ground cinnamon

Preheat oven to 325 degrees F. Line an 8x8x2-inch baking pan with foil. Spray foil with cooking spray and set aside. Combine granola, oats, nuts, flour and raisins in a large mixing bowl. Stir together egg, brown sugar, oil, honey and cinnamon in a small bowl. Stir into granola mixture until well combined. Press evenly into the prepared pan. Bake for 25 to 30 minutes or until lightly browned around the edges. Cool on a wire rack. Lift foil to remove from pan. Cut into bars.

Nutritional Information: 94 calories, 2g protein, 14g carbohydrates, 1g fiber, 4g fat, 9mg cholesterol, 15mg sodium

Live It Tracker: 1 oz-eq grain

Caprese Salad Pita Pockets

1 cup cherry or tomatoes, quartered
4 ounces fresh mozzarella cheese, cubed
1 cup coarsely chopped cucumber
¾ cup mixed spring salad greens
¼ cup fresh basil leaves
2 tablespoons chopped green onion
1 tablespoon red wine vinegar
1 tablespoon olive oil
¼ teaspoon salt
⅛ teaspoon ground black pepper
4 large whole wheat pita bread rounds, halved crosswise
Large soft lettuce leaves

In a medium bowl toss tomatoes, cheese cubes, cucumber, salad greens, basil, green onion, vinegar, oil, salt, and pepper. Line insides of pita halves with lettuce leaves. Spoon tomato mixture into pitas. If desired, wrap each pita in plastic wrap and chill for up to 2 hours before serving. Serves 4

Nutritional Information: 288 Calories; 11g Fat; 13g Protein; 34g Carbohydrate; 2g Fiber; 30mg Cholesterol; 240mg Sodium

Live It Tracker: 3 oz-eq grain; ¾ dairy, ½ cup vegetable

Skillet Lasagna

Nonstick cooking spray
8 ounces extra-lean ground beef (93% lean)
¾ cup chopped green pepper
½ cup chopped onion
2 cloves garlic, minced
1 23.5 ounce jar pasta sauce
1 cup water
2 cups packaged sliced fresh mushrooms
3 cups dried wide egg noodles
½ cup light ricotta cheese
2 tablespoons grated Parmesan or Romano cheese
½ teaspoon dried Italian seasoning, crushed
½ cup shredded part-skim mozzarella cheese (2 oz.)

Coat an extra-large nonstick skillet with cooking spray; heat skillet over medium heat. Cook beef, sweet pepper, onion, and garlic until meat is browned; stirring to break up meat as it cooks. Drain off any fat. Stir in pasta sauce and water. Bring to a boil. Add mushrooms and uncooked noodles; stir to separate noodles. Return to boiling and reduce heat. Cover and gently boil about 10 minutes or until pasta is tender, stirring occasionally. Meanwhile, in a bowl stir together ricotta, Parmesan, and Italian seasoning. Drop cheese mixture by spoonfuls into 10 small mounds (about 1 tablespoon each) on top of pasta mixture in skillet. Sprinkle each mound with mozzarella. Reduce heat to low. Cook, covered, 4 to 5 minutes or until cheese mixture is heated and mozzarella is melted. Serve immediately. Serves 5

Nutritional Information: 315 calories, 9g fat, 61mg cholesterol 61mg, 37g carbohydrates, 3g fat, 4g fiber, 21g protein, 556 sodium

Live It Tracker: 1 oz-eq grain, 2 oz protein, 1 cup Vegetable

STEPS FOR SPIRITUAL GROWTH

—— GOD'S WORD FOR YOUR LIFE

I have hidden your word in my heart that I might not sin against you.

Psalm 119:11

As you begin to make decisions based on what God's Word teaches you, you will want to memorize what He has promised to those who trust and follow Him. Second Peter 1:3 tells us that God "has given us everything we need for life and godliness through our knowledge of him" (emphasis added). The Bible provides instruction and encouragement for any area of life in which you may be struggling. If you are dealing with a particular emotion or traumatic life event—fear, discouragement, stress, financial upset, the death of a loved one, a relationship difficulty—you can search through a Bible concordance for Scripture passages that deal with that particular situation. Scripture provides great comfort to those who memorize it.

One of the promises of knowing and obeying God's Word is that it gives you wisdom, insight, and understanding above all worldly knowledge (see Psalm 119:97–104). Psalm 119:129–130 says, "Your statutes are wonderful; therefore I obey them. The unfolding of your words gives light; it gives understanding to the simple." Now that's a precious promise about guidance for life!

The Value of Scripture Memory

Scripture memory is an important part of the Christian life. There are four key reasons to memorize Scripture:

11. **TO HANDLE DIFFICULT SITUATIONS.** A heartfelt knowledge of God's Word will equip you to handle any situation that you might face. Declaring such truth as, "I can do everything through Christ" (see Philippians 4:13) and "he will never leave me or forsake me" (see Hebrews 13:5) will enable you to walk through situations with peace and courage.

12. **TO OVERCOME TEMPTATION.** Luke 4:1–13 describes how Jesus used Scripture to overcome His temptations in the desert (see also Matthew 4:1-11). Knowledge of Scripture and the strength that comes with the ability to use it are important parts of putting on the full armor of God in preparation for spiritual warfare (see Ephesians 6:10–18).

13. **TO GET GUIDANCE.** Psalm 119:105 states the Word of God "is a lamp to my feet and a light for my path." You learn to hide God's Word in your heart so His light will direct your decisions and actions throughout your day.

14. **TO TRANSFORM YOUR MIND.** "Do not conform any longer to the pattern of this world, but be transformed by the renewing of your mind" (Romans 12:2). Scripture memory allows you to replace a lie with the truth of God's Word. When Scripture becomes firmly settled in your memory, not only will your thoughts connect with God's thoughts, but you will also be able to honor God with small everyday decisions as well as big life-impacting ones. Scripture memorization is the key to making a permanent lifestyle change in your thought patterns, which brings balance to every other area of your life.

Scripture Memory Tips

- Write the verse down, saying it aloud as you write it.
- Read verses before and after the memory verse to get its context.
- Read the verse several times, emphasizing a different word each time.
- Connect the Scripture reference to the first few words.
- Locate patterns, phrases, or keywords.
- Apply the Scripture to circumstances you are now experiencing.
- Pray the verse, making it personal to your life and inserting your name as the recipient of the promise or teaching. (Try that with 1 Corinthians 10:13, inserting "me" and "I" for "you.")
- Review the verse every day until it becomes second nature to think those words whenever your circumstances match its message. The Holy Spirit will bring the verse to mind when you need it most if you decide to plant it in your memory.

Scripture Memorization Made Easy!

What is your learning style? Do you learn by hearing, by sight, or by doing?

If you learn by hearing—if you are an auditory learner—singing the Scripture memory verses, reading them aloud, or recording them and listening to your recording will be very helpful in the memorization process.

If you are a visual learner, writing the verses and repeatedly reading through them will cement them in your mind.

If you learn by doing—if you are a tactile learner—creating motions for the words or using sign language will enable you to more easily recall the verse.

After determining your learning style, link your Scripture memory with a daily task, such as driving to work, walking on a treadmill, or eating lunch. Use these daily tasks as opportunities to memorize and review your verses.

Meals at home or out with friends can be used as a time to share the verse you are memorizing with those at your table. You could close your personal email messages by typing in your weekly memory verse. Or why not say your memory verse every time you brush your teeth or put on your shoes?

The purpose of Scripture memorization is to be able to apply God's words to your life. If you memorize Scripture using methods that connect with your particular learning style, you will find it easier to hide God's Word in your heart.

—— ESTABLISHING A QUIET TIME

Like all other components of the First Place for Health program, developing a live relationship with God is not a random act. You must intentionally seek God if you are to find Him! It's not that God plays hide-and-seek with you. He is always available to you. He invites you to come boldly into His presence. He reveals Himself to you in the pages of the Bible. And once you decide to earnestly seek Him, you are sure to find Him! When you delight in Him, your gracious God will give you the desires of your heart. Spending time getting to know God involves four basic elements: a priority, a plan, a place, and practice.

A Priority

You can successfully establish a quiet time with God by making this meeting a daily priority. This may require carving out time in your day so you have time and space for this new relationship you are cultivating. Often this will mean eliminating less important things so you will have time and space to meet with God. When speaking about Jesus, John the Baptist said, "He must become greater; I must become less" (John 3:30). You will undoubtedly find that to be true as well. What might you need to eliminate from your current schedule so that spending quality time with God can become a priority?

A Plan

Having made quiet time a priority, you will want to come up with a plan. This plan will include the time you have set aside to spend with God and a general outline of how you will spend your time in God's presence.

Elements you should consider incorporating into your quiet time include:

- Singing a song of praise
- Reading a daily selection in a devotional book or reading a psalm
- Using a systematic Scripture reading plan so you will be exposed to the whole truth of God's Word
- Completing your First Place for Health Bible study for that day
- Praying—silent, spoken, and written prayer
- Writing in your spiritual journal.

You will also want to make a list of the materials you will need to make your encounter with God more meaningful:

- A Bible
- Your First Place for Health Bible study
- Your prayer journal
- A pen and/or pencil
- A devotional book
- A Bible concordance
- A college-level dictionary
- A box of tissues (tears—both of sadness and joy—are often part of our quiet time with God!)

Think of how you would plan an important business meeting or social event, and then transfer that knowledge to your meeting time with God.

A Place

Having formulated a meeting-with-God plan, you will next need to create a meeting-with-God place. Of course, God is always with you; however, in order to have quality devotional time with Him, it is desirable that you find a comfortable meeting place. You will want to select a spot that is quiet and as distraction-free as possible. Meeting with God in the same place on a regular basis will help you remember what you are there for: to have an encounter with the true and living God!

Having selected the place, put the materials you have determined to use in your quiet time into a basket or on a nearby table or shelf. Now take the time to establish your personal quiet time with God. Tailor your quiet time to fit your needs—and the time you have allotted to spend with God. Although many people elect to meet with God early in the morning, for others afternoon or evening is best. There is no hard-and-fast rule about when your quiet time should be—the only essential thing is that you establish a quiet time!

Start with a small amount of time that you know you can devote yourself to daily. You can be confident that as you consistently spend time with God each day, the amount of time you can spend will increase as you are ready for the next level of your walk with God.

I will meet with God from _____ to _____ daily.

I plan to use that time with God to _____

_____

Supplies I will need to assemble include _____

_____

My meeting place with God will be _____

_____

Practice

After you have chosen the time and place to meet God each day and you have assembled your supplies, there are four easy steps for having a fruitful and worshipful time with the Lord.

STEP 1: Clear Your Heart and Mind

"Be still, and know that I am God" (Psalm 46:10). Begin your quiet time by reading the daily Bible selection from a devotional guide or a psalm. If you are new in your Christian walk, an excellent devotional guide to use is *Streams in the Desert* by L.B. Cowman. More mature Christians might benefit from My Utmost for His Highest by Oswald Chambers. Of course, you can use any devotional that has a strong emphasis on Scripture and prayer.

STEP 2: Read and Interact with Scripture

"I have hidden your word in my heart that I might not sin against you" (Psalm 119:11). As you open your Bible, ask the Holy Spirit to reveal something He knows you need for this day through the reading of His Word. Always try to find a nugget to encourage or direct you through the day. As you read the passage, pay special attention to the words and phrases the Holy Spirit brings to your attention. Some words may seem to resonate in your soul. You will want to spend time meditating on the passage, asking God what lesson He is teaching you.

After reading the Scripture passage over several times, ask yourself the following questions:

- In light of what I have read today, is there something I must now do? (Confess a sin? Claim a promise? Follow an example? Obey a command? Avoid a situation?)
- How should I respond to what I've read today?

STEP 3: Pray

"Be clear minded and self-controlled so that you can pray" (1 Peter 4:7). Spend time conversing with the Lord in prayer. Prayer is such an important part of First Place for Health that there is an entire section in this member's guide devoted to the practice of prayer.

STEP 4: Praise

"Praise the LORD, O my soul, and forget not all his benefits" (Psalm 103:2). End your quiet time with a time of praise. Be sure to thank the Lord of heaven and warmth for choosing to spend time with you!

—— SHARING YOUR FAITH

Nothing is more effective in drawing someone to Jesus than sharing personal life experiences. People are more open to the good news of Jesus Christ when they see faith in action. Personal faith stories are simple and effective ways to share what Christ is doing in your life, because they show firsthand how Christ makes a difference.

Sharing your faith story has an added benefit: it builds you up in your faith, too! Is your experience in First Place for Health providing you opportunities to share with others what God is doing in your life? If you answered yes, then you have a personal faith story!

If you do not have a personal faith story, perhaps it is because you don't know Jesus Christ as your personal Lord and Savior. Read through "Steps to Becoming a Christian" (which is the next chapter) and begin today to give Christ first place in your life.

Creativity and preparation in using opportunities to share a word or story about Jesus is an important part of the Christian life. Is Jesus helping you in a special way? Are you achieving a level of success or peace that you haven't experienced in other attempts to lose weight, exercise regularly, or eat healthier? As people see you making changes and achieving success, they may ask you how you are doing it. How will—or do—you respond? Remember, your story is unique, and it may allow others to see what Christ is doing in your life. It may also help to bring Christ into the life of another person.

Personal Statements of Faith

First Place for Health gives you a great opportunity to communicate your faith and express what God is doing in your life. Be ready to use your own personal statement of faith whenever the opportunity presents itself. Personal statements of faith should be short and fit naturally into a conversation. They don't require or expect any action or response from the listener. The goal is not to get another person to change but simply to help you communicate who you are and what's important to you.

Here are some examples of short statements of faith that you might use when someone asks what you are doing to lose weight:

- "I've been meeting with a group at my church. We pray together, support each other, learn about nutrition, and study the Bible."
- "It's amazing how Bible study and prayer are helping me lose weight and eat healthier."
- "I've had a lot of support from a group I meet with at church."
- "I'm relying more on God to help me make changes in my lifestyle."

Begin keeping a list of your meaningful experiences as you go through the First Place for Health program. Also notice what is happening in the lives of others. Use the following questions to help you prepare short personal statements and stories of faith:

- What is God doing in your life physically, mentally, emotionally, and spiritually?
- How has your relationship with God changed? Is it more intimate or personal?
- How is prayer, Bible study, and/or the support of others helping you achieve your goals for a healthy weight and good nutrition?

Writing Your Personal Faith Story

Write a brief story about how God is working in your life through First Place for Health. Use your story to help you share with others what's happening in your life.

Use the following questions to help develop your story:

- Why did you join First Place for Health? What specific circumstances led you to a Christ-centered health and weight-loss program? What were you feeling when you joined?
- What was your relationship with Christ when you started First Place for Health? What is it now?
- Has your experience in First Place for Health changed your relationship with Christ? With yourself? With others?
- How has your relationship with Christ, prayer, Bible study, and group support made a difference in your life?
- What specific verse or passage of Scripture has made a difference in the way you view yourself or your relationship with Christ?
- What experiences have impacted your life since starting First Place for Health?
- In what ways is Christ working in your life today? In what ways is He meeting your needs?
- How has Christ worked in other members of your First Place for Health group?

Answer the above questions in a few sentences, and then use your answers to help you write your own short personal faith story.

MEMBER SURVEY

We would love to know more about you. Share this form with your leader.

Name _____   Birth date _____

Tell us about your family.

_____

_____

_____

_____

Would you like to receive more information   Yes   No
about our church?

What area of expertise would you be willing to share with our class?

_____

_____

Why did you join First Place for Health?

_____

_____

With notice, would you be willing to lead a Bible study   Yes   No
discussion one week?

Are you comfortable praying out loud? _____

Would you be willing to assist recording weights and/or   Yes   No
evaluating the Live It Trackers?

Any other comments:

_____

_____

PERSONAL WEIGHT AND MEASUREMENT RECORD

WEEK	WEIGHT	+ OR -	GOAL THIS SESSION	POUNDS TO GOAL
1				
2				
3				
4				
5				
6				
7				
8				
9				
10				
11				
12				

BEGINNING MEASUREMENTS

WAIST _____ HIPS _____ THIGHS _____ CHEST _____

ENDING MEASUREMENTS

WAIST _____ HIPS _____ THIGHS _____ CHEST _____

And when they heard that the Lord was concerned about them and had seen their misery,
they bowed down and worshiped. Exodus 4:31

Date: _____

Name: _____

Home Phone: _____

Cell Phone: _____

Email: _____

Personal Prayer Concerns

_____

_____

_____

_____

_____

_____

_____

This form is for prayer requests that are personal to you and your journey in First Place for Health. Please complete and have it ready to turn in when you arrive at your group meeting.

Moses answered the people, "Do not be afraid. Stand firm and you
will see the deliverance the Lord will bring you today."
Exodus 14:13

Date: _____

Name: _____

Home Phone: _____

Cell Phone: _____

Email: _____

Personal Prayer Concerns

_____

_____

_____

_____

_____

_____

_____

This form is for prayer requests that are personal to you and your journey in First Place for Health.
Please complete and have it ready to turn in when you arrive at your group meeting.

And he said to Moses, "Please, my lord, do not hold against us the sin we have so foolishly committed." Numbers 12:11

Date: _____

Name: _____

Home Phone: _____

Cell Phone: _____

Email: _____

Personal Prayer Concerns

_____

_____

_____

_____

_____

_____

_____

_____

This form is for prayer requests that are personal to you and your journey in First Place for Health. Please complete and have it ready to turn in when you arrive at your group meeting.

The Lord answered Moses, "Is the Lord's arm too short? You will now
see whether or not what I say will come true for you."
Numbers 11:23

Date: _____

Name: _____

Home Phone: _____

Cell Phone: _____

Email: _____

Personal Prayer Concerns

_____

_____

_____

_____

_____

_____

_____

This form is for prayer requests that are personal to you and your journey in First Place for Health.
Please complete and have it ready to turn in when you arrive at your group meeting.

*Now if you obey me fully and keep my covenant, then out of all nations you will be
my treasured possession. Exodus 19:5*

Date: _____

Name: _____

Home Phone: _____

Cell Phone: _____

Email: _____

Personal Prayer Concerns

_____

_____

_____

_____

_____

_____

_____

This form is for prayer requests that are personal to you and your journey in First Place for Health.
Please complete and have it ready to turn in when you arrive at your group meeting.

The Lord said to Moses, "Come up to me on the mountain and stay here."
Exodus 24:12

Date: _____

Name: _____

Home Phone: _____

Cell Phone: _____

Email: _____

Personal Prayer Concerns

_____

_____

_____

_____

_____

_____

_____

This form is for prayer requests that are personal to you and your journey in First Place for Health. Please complete and have it ready to turn in when you arrive at your group meeting.

The Lord replied, "My Presence will go with you, and I will give you rest."
Exodus 33:14

Date: _____

Name: _____

Home Phone: _____

Cell Phone: _____

Email: _____

Personal Prayer Concerns

_____

_____

_____

_____

_____

_____

_____

_____

This form is for prayer requests that are personal to you and your journey in First Place for Health. Please complete and have it ready to turn in when you arrive at your group meeting.

"The Lord himself goes before you and will be with you; he will never leave you nor forsake you.
Do not be afraid; do not be discouraged."
Deuteronomy 31:8

Date: _____

Name: _____

Home Phone: _____

Cell Phone: _____

Email: _____

Personal Prayer Concern

_____

_____

_____

_____

_____

_____

_____

This form is for prayer requests that are personal to you and your journey in First Place for Health. Please complete and have it ready to turn in when you arrive at your group meeting.

Date: _____

Name: _____

Home Phone: _____

Cell Phone: _____

Email: _____

Personal Prayer Concerns

_____

_____

_____

_____

_____

_____

_____

_____

This form is for prayer requests that are personal to you and your journey in First Place for Health. Please complete and have it ready to turn in when you arrive at your group meeting.

LIVE IT TRACKER

Name: _____   Date: _____ Week #: _____

My activity goal for next week: loss /gain _____ Calorie Range: _____
○ None   ○ <30 min/day   ○ 30-60 min/day
                                         My week at a glance:
                                         ○ Great   ○ So-so   ○ Not so great
My food goal for next week: _____
                                         Activity level:
_____   ○ None   ○ <30 min/day   ○ 30-60 min/day

RECOMMENDED DAILY AMOUNT OF FOOD FROM EACH GROUP

GROUP	DAILY CALORIES							
	1300-1400	1500-1600	1700-1800	1900-2000	2100-2200	2300-2400	2500-2600	2700-2800
Fruits	1.5 – 2 c.	1.5 – 2 c.	1.5 – 2 c.	2 – 2.5 c.	2 – 2.5 c.	2.5 – 3.5 c.	3.5 – 4.5 c.	3.5 – 4.5 c.
Vegetables	1.5 – 2 c.	2 – 2.5 c.	2.5 – 3 c.	2.5 – 3 c.	3 – 3.5 c.	3.5 – 4.5 c.	4.5 – 5 c.	4.5 – 5 c.
Grains	5 oz eq.	5-6 oz eq.	6-7 oz eq.	6-7 oz eq.	7-8 oz eq.	8-9 oz eq.	9-10 oz eq.	10-11 oz eq.
Dairy	2-3 c.	3 c.	3 c.	3 c.	3 c.	3 c.	3 c.	3 c.
Protein	4 oz eq.	5 oz eq.	5-5.5 oz eq.	5.5-6.5 oz eq.	6.5-7 oz eq.	7-7.5 oz eq.	7-7.5 oz eq.	7.5-8 oz eq.
Healthy Oils & Other Fats	4 tsp.	5 tsp.	5 tsp.	6 tsp.	6 tsp.	7 tsp.	8 tsp.	8 tsp.
Water & Super Beverages*	Women: 9 c. Men: 13 c.	Women: 9 c. Men: 13 c.	Women: 9 c. Men: 13 c.	Women: 9 c. Men: 13 c.	Women: 9 c. Men: 13 c.	Women: 9 c. Men: 13 c.	Women: 9 c. Men: 13 c.	Women: 9 c. Men: 13 c.

*May count up to 3 cups caffeinated tea or coffee toward goal

DAILY FOOD GROUP TRACKER

GROUP	FRUITS	VEGETABLES	GRAINS	PROTEIN	DAIRY	HEALTHY OILS & OTHER FATS	WATER & SUPER BEVERAGES
1 Estimate Total							
2 Estimate Total							
3 Estimate Total							
4 Estimate Total							
5 Estimate Total							
6 Estimate Total							
7 Estimate Total							

FOOD CHOICES   DAY 1

Breakfast: _____
Lunch: _____
Dinner: _____
Snacks: _____

PHYSICAL ACTIVITY   steps/miles/minutes: _____   ### SPIRITUAL ACTIVITY

description: _____   description: _____

FOOD CHOICES

DAY ❷

Breakfast: _____

Lunch: _____

Dinner: _____

Snacks: _____

PHYSICAL ACTIVITY steps/miles/minutes:_____

description: _____

SPIRITUAL ACTIVITY

description: _____

FOOD CHOICES

DAY ❸

Breakfast: _____

Lunch: _____

Dinner: _____

Snacks: _____

PHYSICAL ACTIVITY steps/miles/minutes:_____

description: _____

SPIRITUAL ACTIVITY

description: _____

FOOD CHOICES

DAY ❹

Breakfast: _____

Lunch: _____

Dinner: _____

Snacks: _____

PHYSICAL ACTIVITY steps/miles/minutes:_____

description: _____

SPIRITUAL ACTIVITY

description: _____

FOOD CHOICES

DAY ❺

Breakfast: _____

Lunch: _____

Dinner: _____

Snacks: _____

PHYSICAL ACTIVITY steps/miles/minutes:_____

description: _____

SPIRITUAL ACTIVITY

description: _____

FOOD CHOICES

DAY ❻

Breakfast: _____

Lunch: _____

Dinner: _____

Snacks: _____

PHYSICAL ACTIVITY steps/miles/minutes:_____

description: _____

SPIRITUAL ACTIVITY

description: _____

FOOD CHOICES

DAY ❼

Breakfast: _____

Lunch: _____

Dinner: _____

Snacks: _____

PHYSICAL ACTIVITY steps/miles/minutes:_____

description: _____

SPIRITUAL ACTIVITY

description: _____

Name: _____

Date: _____ Week #: _____

My activity goal for next week:
○ None ○ <30 min/day ○ 30-60 min/day

My food goal for next week: _____

loss/gain _____ Calorie Range: _____

My week at a glance:
○ Great ○ So-so ○ Not so great

Activity level:
○ None ○ <30 min/day ○ 30-60 min/day

RECOMMENDED DAILY AMOUNT OF FOOD FROM EACH GROUP

GROUP	DAILY CALORIES							
....	1300-1400	1500-1600	1700-1800	1900-2000	2100-2200	2300-2400	2500-2600	2700-2800
Fruits	1.5 – 2 c.	1.5 – 2 c.	1.5 – 2 c.	2 – 2.5 c.	2 – 2.5 c.	2.5 – 3.5 c.	3.5 – 4.5 c.	3.5 – 4.5 c.
Vegetables	1.5 – 2 c.	2 – 2.5 c.	2.5 – 3 c.	2.5 – 3 c.	3 – 3.5 c.	3.5 – 4.5 c.	4.5 – 5 c.	4.5 – 5 c.
Grains	5 oz eq.	5-6 oz eq.	6-7 oz eq.	6-7 oz eq.	7-8 oz eq.	8-9 oz eq.	9-10 oz eq.	10-11 oz eq.
Dairy	2-3 c.	3 c.	3 c.	3 c.	3 c.	3 c.	3 c.	3 c.
Protein	4 oz eq.	5 oz eq.	5-5.5 oz eq.	5.5-6.5 oz eq.	6.5-7 oz eq.	7-7.5 oz eq.	7-7.5 oz eq.	7.5-8 oz eq.
Healthy Oils & Other Fats	4 tsp.	5 tsp.	5 tsp.	6 tsp.	6 tsp.	7 tsp.	8 tsp.	8 tsp.
Water & Super Beverages*	Women: 9 c. Men: 13 c.	Women: 9 c. Men: 13 c.	Women: 9 c. Men: 13 c.	Women: 9 c. Men: 13 c.	Women: 9 c. Men: 13 c.	Women: 9 c. Men: 13 c.	Women: 9 c. Men: 13 c.	Women: 9 c. Men: 13 c.

*May count up to 3 cups caffeinated tea or coffee toward goal

DAILY FOOD GROUP TRACKER

GROUP	FRUITS	VEGETABLES	GRAINS	PROTEIN	DAIRY	HEALTHY OILS & OTHER FATS	WATER & SUPER BEVERAGES
1 Estimate Total							
2 Estimate Total							
3 Estimate Total							
4 Estimate Total							
5 Estimate Total							
6 Estimate Total							
7 Estimate Total							

FOOD CHOICES **DAY ❶**

Breakfast: _____
Lunch: _____
Dinner: _____
Snacks: _____

PHYSICAL ACTIVITY steps/miles/minutes: _____

description: _____

SPIRITUAL ACTIVITY

description: _____

FOOD CHOICES   DAY ❷

Breakfast: _____

Lunch: _____

Dinner: _____

Snacks: _____

PHYSICAL ACTIVITY   steps/miles/minutes: _____   SPIRITUAL ACTIVITY

description: _____   description: _____

FOOD CHOICES   DAY ❸

Breakfast: _____

Lunch: _____

Dinner: _____

Snacks: _____

PHYSICAL ACTIVITY   steps/miles/minutes: _____   SPIRITUAL ACTIVITY

description: _____   description: _____

FOOD CHOICES   DAY ❹

Breakfast: _____

Lunch: _____

Dinner: _____

Snacks: _____

PHYSICAL ACTIVITY   steps/miles/minutes: _____   SPIRITUAL ACTIVITY

description: _____   description: _____

FOOD CHOICES   DAY ❺

Breakfast: _____

Lunch: _____

Dinner: _____

Snacks: _____

PHYSICAL ACTIVITY   steps/miles/minutes: _____   SPIRITUAL ACTIVITY

description: _____   description: _____

FOOD CHOICES   DAY ❻

Breakfast: _____

Lunch: _____

Dinner: _____

Snacks: _____

PHYSICAL ACTIVITY   steps/miles/minutes: _____   SPIRITUAL ACTIVITY

description: _____   description: _____

FOOD CHOICES   DAY ❼

Breakfast: _____

Lunch: _____

Dinner: _____

Snacks: _____

PHYSICAL ACTIVITY   steps/miles/minutes: _____   SPIRITUAL ACTIVITY

description: _____   description: _____

LIVE IT TRACKER

Name: _____

Date: _____ Week #: _____

My activity goal for next week:
○ None ○ <30 min/day ○ 30-60 min/day

loss / gain _____ Calorie Range: _____

My week at a glance:
○ Great ○ So-so ○ Not so great

My food goal for next week: _____

Activity level:
○ None ○ <30 min/day ○ 30-60 min/day

RECOMMENDED DAILY AMOUNT OF FOOD FROM EACH GROUP

GROUP	DAILY CALORIES							
......	1300-1400	1500-1600	1700-1800	1900-2000	2100-2200	2300-2400	2500-2600	2700-2800
Fruits	1.5 – 2 c.	1.5 – 2 c.	1.5 – 2 c.	2 – 2.5 c.	2 – 2.5 c.	2.5 – 3.5 c.	3.5 – 4.5 c.	3.5 – 4.5 c.
Vegetables	1.5 – 2 c.	2 – 2.5 c.	2.5 – 3 c.	2.5 – 3 c.	3 – 3.5 c.	3.5 – 4.5 c..	4.5 – 5 c.	4.5 – 5 c.
Grains	5 oz eq.	5-6 oz eq.	6-7 oz eq.	6-7 oz eq.	7-8 oz eq.	8-9 oz eq.	9-10 oz eq.	10-11 oz eq.
Dairy	2-3 c.	3 c.	3 c.	3 c.	3 c.	3 c.	3 c.	3 c.
Protein	4 oz eq.	5 oz eq.	5-5.5 oz eq.	5.5-6.5 oz eq.	6.5-7 oz eq.	7-7.5 oz eq.	7-7.5 oz eq.	7.5-8 oz eq.
Healthy Oils & Other Fats	4 tsp.	5 tsp.	5 tsp.	6 tsp.	6 tsp.	7 tsp.	8 tsp.	8 tsp.
Water & Super Beverages*	Women: 9 c. Men: 13 c.	Women: 9 c. Men: 13 c.	Women: 9 c. Men: 13 c.	Women: 9 c. Men: 13 c.	Women: 9 c. Men: 13 c.	Women: 9 c. Men: 13 c.	Women: 9 c. Men: 13 c.	Women: 9 c. Men: 13 c.

*May count up to 3 cups caffeinated tea or coffee toward goal

DAILY FOOD GROUP TRACKER

GROUP	FRUITS	VEGETABLES	GRAINS	PROTEIN	DAIRY	HEALTHY OILS & OTHER FATS	WATER & SUPER BEVERAGES
1 Estimate Total							
2 Estimate Total							
3 Estimate Total							
4 Estimate Total							
5 Estimate Total							
6 Estimate Total							
7 Estimate Total							

FOOD CHOICES   DAY ❶

Breakfast: _____
Lunch: _____
Dinner: _____
Snacks: _____

PHYSICAL ACTIVITY   steps/miles/minutes: _____

description: _____

SPIRITUAL ACTIVITY

description: _____

FOOD CHOICES — DAY 2

Breakfast: _____
Lunch: _____
Dinner: _____
Snacks: _____

PHYSICAL ACTIVITY   steps/miles/minutes: _____   SPIRITUAL ACTIVITY

description: _____   description: _____

FOOD CHOICES — DAY 3

Breakfast: _____
Lunch: _____
Dinner: _____
Snacks: _____

PHYSICAL ACTIVITY   steps/miles/minutes: _____   SPIRITUAL ACTIVITY

description: _____   description: _____

FOOD CHOICES — DAY 4

Breakfast: _____
Lunch: _____
Dinner: _____
Snacks: _____

PHYSICAL ACTIVITY   steps/miles/minutes: _____   SPIRITUAL ACTIVITY

description: _____   description: _____

FOOD CHOICES — DAY 5

Breakfast: _____
Lunch: _____
Dinner: _____
Snacks: _____

PHYSICAL ACTIVITY   steps/miles/minutes: _____   SPIRITUAL ACTIVITY

description: _____   description: _____

FOOD CHOICES — DAY 6

Breakfast: _____
Lunch: _____
Dinner: _____
Snacks: _____

PHYSICAL ACTIVITY   steps/miles/minutes: _____   SPIRITUAL ACTIVITY

description: _____   description: _____

FOOD CHOICES — DAY 7

Breakfast: _____
Lunch: _____
Dinner: _____
Snacks: _____

PHYSICAL ACTIVITY   steps/miles/minutes: _____   SPIRITUAL ACTIVITY

description: _____   description: _____

Name: _____   Date: _____ Week #: _____

My activity goal for next week: loss / gain _____ Calorie Range: _____
○ None   ○ <30 min/day   ○ 30-60 min/day
                                         My week at a glance:
                                         ○ Great   ○ So-so   ○ Not so great

My food goal for next week: _____
                                         Activity level:
_____   ○ None   ○ <30 min/day   ○ 30-60 min/day

RECOMMENDED DAILY AMOUNT OF FOOD FROM EACH GROUP

GROUP	DAILY CALORIES							
....	1300-1400	1500-1600	1700-1800	1900-2000	2100-2200	2300-2400	2500-2600	2700-2800
Fruits	1.5 – 2 c.	1.5 – 2 c.	1.5 – 2 c.	2 – 2.5 c.	2 – 2.5 c.	2.5 – 3.5 c.	3.5 – 4.5 c.	3.5 – 4.5 c.
Vegetables	1.5 – 2 c.	2 – 2.5 c.	2.5 – 3 c.	2.5 – 3 c.	3 – 3.5 c.	3.5 – 4.5 c.	4.5 – 5 c.	4.5 – 5 c.
Grains	5 oz eq.	5-6 oz eq.	6-7 oz eq.	6-7 oz eq.	7-8 oz eq.	8-9 oz eq.	9-10 oz eq.	10-11 oz eq.
Dairy	2-3 c.	3 c.	3 c.	3 c.	3 c.	3 c.	3 c.	3 c.
Protein	4 oz eq.	5 oz eq.	5-5.5 oz eq.	5.5-6.5 oz eq.	6.5-7 oz eq.	7-7.5 oz eq.	7-7.5 oz eq.	7.5-8 oz eq.
Healthy Oils & Other Fats	4 tsp.	5 tsp.	5 tsp.	6 tsp.	6 tsp.	7 tsp.	8 tsp.	8 tsp.
Water & Super Beverages*	Women: 9 c. Men: 13 c.	Women: 9 c. Men: 13 c.	Women: 9 c. Men: 13 c.	Women: 9 c. Men: 13 c.	Women: 9 c. Men: 13 c.	Women: 9 c. Men: 13 c.	Women: 9 c. Men: 13 c.	Women: 9 c. Men: 13 c.

*May count up to 3 cups caffeinated tea or coffee toward goal

DAILY FOOD GROUP TRACKER

GROUP	FRUITS	VEGETABLES	GRAINS	PROTEIN	DAIRY	HEALTHY OILS & OTHER FATS	WATER & SUPER BEVERAGES
1 Estimate Total							
2 Estimate Total							
3 Estimate Total							
4 Estimate Total							
5 Estimate Total							
6 Estimate Total							
7 Estimate Total							

FOOD CHOICES   **DAY 1**

Breakfast: _____

Lunch: _____

Dinner: _____

Snacks: _____

PHYSICAL ACTIVITY   steps/miles/minutes: _____   **SPIRITUAL ACTIVITY**

description: _____   description: _____

_____   _____

FOOD CHOICES   DAY ❷

Breakfast: _____

Lunch: _____

Dinner: _____

Snacks: _____

PHYSICAL ACTIVITY   steps/miles/minutes: _____   SPIRITUAL ACTIVITY

description: _____   description: _____

FOOD CHOICES   DAY ❸

Breakfast: _____

Lunch: _____

Dinner: _____

Snacks: _____

PHYSICAL ACTIVITY   steps/miles/minutes: _____   SPIRITUAL ACTIVITY

description: _____   description: _____

FOOD CHOICES   DAY ❹

Breakfast: _____

Lunch: _____

Dinner: _____

Snacks: _____

PHYSICAL ACTIVITY   steps/miles/minutes: _____   SPIRITUAL ACTIVITY

description: _____   description: _____

FOOD CHOICES   DAY ❺

Breakfast: _____

Lunch: _____

Dinner: _____

Snacks: _____

PHYSICAL ACTIVITY   steps/miles/minutes: _____   SPIRITUAL ACTIVITY

description: _____   description: _____

FOOD CHOICES   DAY ❻

Breakfast: _____

Lunch: _____

Dinner: _____

Snacks: _____

PHYSICAL ACTIVITY   steps/miles/minutes: _____   SPIRITUAL ACTIVITY

description: _____   description: _____

FOOD CHOICES   DAY ❼

Breakfast: _____

Lunch: _____

Dinner: _____

Snacks: _____

PHYSICAL ACTIVITY   steps/miles/minutes: _____   SPIRITUAL ACTIVITY

description: _____   description: _____

Name: _____   Date: _____ Week #: _____

My activity goal for next week:
○ None   ○ <30 min/day   ○ 30-60 min/day

loss /gain _____   Calorie Range: _____

My week at a glance:
○ Great   ○ So-so   ○ Not so great

My food goal for next week: _____

Activity level:
○ None   ○ <30 min/day   ○ 30-60 min/day

RECOMMENDED DAILY AMOUNT OF FOOD FROM EACH GROUP

GROUP	DAILY CALORIES							
	1300-1400	1500-1600	1700-1800	1900-2000	2100-2200	2300-2400	2500-2600	2700-2800
Fruits	1.5 – 2 c.	1.5 – 2 c.	1.5 – 2 c.	2 – 2.5 c.	2 – 2.5 c.	2.5 – 3.5 c.	3.5 – 4.5 c.	3.5 – 4.5 c.
Vegetables	1.5 – 2 c.	2 – 2.5 c.	2.5 – 3 c.	2.5 – 3 c.	3 – 3.5 c.	3.5 – 4.5 c..	4.5 – 5 c.	4.5 – 5 c.
Grains	5 oz eq.	5-6 oz eq.	6-7 oz eq.	6-7 oz eq.	7-8 oz eq.	8-9 oz eq.	9-10 oz eq.	10-11 oz eq.
Dairy	2-3 c.	3 c.	3 c.	3 c.	3 c.	3 c.	3 c.	3 c.
Protein	4 oz eq.	5 oz eq.	5-5.5 oz eq.	5.5-6.5 oz eq.	6.5-7 oz eq.	7-7.5 oz eq.	7-7.5 oz eq.	7.5-8 oz eq.
Healthy Oils & Other Fats	4 tsp.	5 tsp.	5 tsp.	6 tsp.	6 tsp.	7 tsp.	8 tsp.	8 tsp.
Water & Super Beverages*	Women: 9 c. Men: 13 c.	Women: 9 c. Men: 13 c.	Women: 9 c. Men: 13 c.	Women: 9 c. Men: 13 c.	Women: 9 c. Men: 13 c.	Women: 9 c. Men: 13 c.	Women: 9 c. Men: 13 c.	Women: 9 c. Men: 13 c.

*May count up to 3 cups caffeinated tea or coffee toward goal

DAILY FOOD GROUP TRACKER

GROUP	FRUITS	VEGETABLES	GRAINS	PROTEIN	DAIRY	HEALTHY OILS & OTHER FATS	WATER & SUPER BEVERAGES
1 Estimate Total							
2 Estimate Total							
3 Estimate Total							
4 Estimate Total							
5 Estimate Total							
6 Estimate Total							
7 Estimate Total							

FOOD CHOICES   DAY ❶

Breakfast: _____
Lunch: _____
Dinner: _____
Snacks: _____

PHYSICAL ACTIVITY   steps/miles/minutes:

description: _____

SPIRITUAL ACTIVITY

description: _____

FOOD CHOICES

DAY ②

Breakfast: _____

Lunch: _____

Dinner: _____

Snacks: _____

| PHYSICAL ACTIVITY | steps/miles/minutes: | SPIRITUAL ACTIVITY |

description: _____ description: _____

FOOD CHOICES

DAY ③

Breakfast: _____

Lunch: _____

Dinner: _____

Snacks: _____

| PHYSICAL ACTIVITY | steps/miles/minutes: | SPIRITUAL ACTIVITY |

description: _____ description: _____

FOOD CHOICES

DAY ④

Breakfast: _____

Lunch: _____

Dinner: _____

Snacks: _____

| PHYSICAL ACTIVITY | steps/miles/minutes: | SPIRITUAL ACTIVITY |

description: _____ description: _____

FOOD CHOICES

DAY ⑤

Breakfast: _____

Lunch: _____

Dinner: _____

Snacks: _____

| PHYSICAL ACTIVITY | steps/miles/minutes: | SPIRITUAL ACTIVITY |

description: _____ description: _____

FOOD CHOICES

DAY ⑥

Breakfast: _____

Lunch: _____

Dinner: _____

Snacks: _____

| PHYSICAL ACTIVITY | steps/miles/minutes: | SPIRITUAL ACTIVITY |

description: _____ description: _____

FOOD CHOICES

DAY ⑦

Breakfast: _____

Lunch: _____

Dinner: _____

Snacks: _____

| PHYSICAL ACTIVITY | steps/miles/minutes: | SPIRITUAL ACTIVITY |

description: _____ description: _____

Name: _____   Date: _____ Week #: _____

My activity goal for next week: loss /gain _____ Calorie Range: _____
○ None   ○ <30 min/day   ○ 30-60 min/day
                                         My week at a glance:
                                         ○ Great   ○ So-so   ○ Not so great
My food goal for next week: _____
                                         Activity level:
                                         ○ None   ○ <30 min/day   ○ 30-60 min/day

RECOMMENDED DAILY AMOUNT OF FOOD FROM EACH GROUP

GROUP	DAILY CALORIES							
	1300-1400	1500-1600	1700-1800	1900-2000	2100-2200	2300-2400	2500-2600	2700-2800
Fruits	1.5 – 2 c.	1.5 – 2 c.	1.5 – 2 c.	2 – 2.5 c.	2 – 2.5 c.	2.5 – 3.5 c.	3.5 – 4.5 c.	3.5 – 4.5 c.
Vegetables	1.5 – 2 c.	2 – 2.5 c.	2.5 – 3 c.	2.5 – 3 c.	3 – 3.5 c.	3.5 – 4.5 c.	4.5 – 5 c.	4.5 – 5 c.
Grains	5 oz eq.	5-6 oz eq.	6-7 oz eq.	6-7 oz eq.	7-8 oz eq.	8-9 oz eq.	9-10 oz eq.	10-11 oz eq.
Dairy	2-3 c.	3 c.	3 c.	3 c.	3 c.	3 c.	3 c.	3 c.
Protein	4 oz eq.	5 oz eq.	5-5.5 oz eq.	5.5-6.5 oz eq.	6.5-7 oz eq.	7-7.5 oz eq.	7-7.5 oz eq.	7.5-8 oz eq.
Healthy Oils & Other Fats	4 tsp.	5 tsp.	5 tsp.	6 tsp.	6 tsp.	7 tsp.	8 tsp.	8 tsp.
Water & Super Beverages*	Women: 9 c. Men: 13 c.	Women: 9 c. Men: 13 c.	Women: 9 c. Men: 13 c.	Women: 9 c. Men: 13 c.	Women: 9 c. Men: 13 c.	Women: 9 c. Men: 13 c.	Women: 9 c. Men: 13 c.	Women: 9 c. Men: 13 c.

*May count up to 3 cups caffeinated tea or coffee toward goal

DAILY FOOD GROUP TRACKER

GROUP	FRUITS	VEGETABLES	GRAINS	PROTEIN	DAIRY	HEALTHY OILS & OTHER FATS	WATER & SUPER BEVERAGES
❶ Estimate Total							
❷ Estimate Total							
❸ Estimate Total							
❹ Estimate Total							
❺ Estimate Total							
❻ Estimate Total							
❼ Estimate Total							

FOOD CHOICES   **DAY ❶**

Breakfast: _____

Lunch: _____

Dinner: _____

Snacks: _____

PHYSICAL ACTIVITY   steps/miles/minutes: _____   **SPIRITUAL ACTIVITY**

description: _____   description: _____

FOOD CHOICES

DAY ❷

Breakfast: _____

Lunch: _____

Dinner: _____

Snacks: _____

PHYSICAL ACTIVITY steps/miles/minutes:	SPIRITUAL ACTIVITY
description:	description:

FOOD CHOICES

DAY ❸

Breakfast: _____

Lunch: _____

Dinner: _____

Snacks: _____

PHYSICAL ACTIVITY steps/miles/minutes:	SPIRITUAL ACTIVITY
description:	description:

FOOD CHOICES

DAY ❹

Breakfast: _____

Lunch: _____

Dinner: _____

Snacks: _____

PHYSICAL ACTIVITY steps/miles/minutes:	SPIRITUAL ACTIVITY
description:	description:

FOOD CHOICES

DAY ❺

Breakfast: _____

Lunch: _____

Dinner: _____

Snacks: _____

PHYSICAL ACTIVITY steps/miles/minutes:	SPIRITUAL ACTIVITY
description:	description:

FOOD CHOICES

DAY ❻

Breakfast: _____

Lunch: _____

Dinner: _____

Snacks: _____

PHYSICAL ACTIVITY steps/miles/minutes:	SPIRITUAL ACTIVITY
description:	description:

FOOD CHOICES

DAY ❼

Breakfast: _____

Lunch: _____

Dinner: _____

Snacks: _____

PHYSICAL ACTIVITY steps/miles/minutes:	SPIRITUAL ACTIVITY
description:	description:

LIVE IT TRACKER

Name: _____ Date: _____ Week #: _____

My activity goal for next week: loss /gain _____ Calorie Range: _____

○ None ○ <30 min/day ○ 30-60 min/day

My week at a glance:
○ Great ○ So-so ○ Not so great

My food goal for next week: _____

Activity level:
○ None ○ <30 min/day ○ 30-60 min/day

RECOMMENDED DAILY AMOUNT OF FOOD FROM EACH GROUP

GROUP	DAILY CALORIES							
	1300-1400	1500-1600	1700-1800	1900-2000	2100-2200	2300-2400	2500-2600	2700-2800
Fruits	1.5 – 2 c.	1.5 – 2 c.	1.5 – 2 c.	2 – 2.5 c.	2 – 2.5 c.	2.5 – 3.5 c.	3.5 – 4.5 c.	3.5 – 4.5 c.
Vegetables	1.5 – 2 c.	2 – 2.5 c.	2.5 – 3 c.	2.5 – 3 c.	3 – 3.5 c.	3.5 – 4.5 c..	4.5 – 5 c.	4.5 – 5 c.
Grains	5 oz eq.	5-6 oz eq.	6-7 oz eq.	6-7 oz eq.	7-8 oz eq.	8-9 oz eq.	9-10 oz eq.	10-11 oz eq.
Dairy	2-3 c.	3 c.	3 c.	3 c.	3 c.	3 c.	3 c.	3 c.
Protein	4 oz eq.	5 oz eq.	5-5.5 oz eq.	5.5-6.5 oz eq.	6.5-7 oz eq.	7-7.5 oz eq.	7-7.5 oz eq.	7.5-8 oz eq.
Healthy Oils & Other Fats	4 tsp.	5 tsp.	5 tsp.	6 tsp.	6 tsp.	7 tsp.	8 tsp.	8 tsp.
Water & Super Beverages*	Women: 9 c. Men: 13 c.	Women: 9 c. Men: 13 c.	Women: 9 c. Men: 13 c.	Women: 9 c. Men: 13 c.	Women: 9 c. Men: 13 c.	Women: 9 c. Men: 13 c.	Women: 9 c. Men: 13 c.	Women: 9 c. Men: 13 c.

*May count up to 3 cups caffeinated tea or coffee toward goal

DAILY FOOD GROUP TRACKER

GROUP	FRUITS	VEGETABLES	GRAINS	PROTEIN	DAIRY	HEALTHY OILS & OTHER FATS	WATER & SUPER BEVERAGES
❶ Estimate Total							
❷ Estimate Total							
❸ Estimate Total							
❹ Estimate Total							
❺ Estimate Total							
❻ Estimate Total							
❼ Estimate Total							

FOOD CHOICES   DAY ❶

Breakfast: _____
Lunch: _____
Dinner: _____
Snacks: _____

PHYSICAL ACTIVITY   steps/miles/minutes: _____   ### SPIRITUAL ACTIVITY

description: _____   description: _____

FOOD CHOICES
DAY ❷

Breakfast: _____
Lunch: _____
Dinner: _____
Snacks: _____

PHYSICAL ACTIVITY steps/miles/minutes: _____
description: _____

SPIRITUAL ACTIVITY
description: _____

FOOD CHOICES
DAY ❸

Breakfast: _____
Lunch: _____
Dinner: _____
Snacks: _____

PHYSICAL ACTIVITY steps/miles/minutes: _____
description: _____

SPIRITUAL ACTIVITY
description: _____

FOOD CHOICES
DAY ❹

Breakfast: _____
Lunch: _____
Dinner: _____
Snacks: _____

PHYSICAL ACTIVITY steps/miles/minutes: _____
description: _____

SPIRITUAL ACTIVITY
description: _____

FOOD CHOICES
DAY ❺

Breakfast: _____
Lunch: _____
Dinner: _____
Snacks: _____

PHYSICAL ACTIVITY steps/miles/minutes: _____
description: _____

SPIRITUAL ACTIVITY
description: _____

FOOD CHOICES
DAY ❻

Breakfast: _____
Lunch: _____
Dinner: _____
Snacks: _____

PHYSICAL ACTIVITY steps/miles/minutes: _____
description: _____

SPIRITUAL ACTIVITY
description: _____

FOOD CHOICES
DAY ❼

Breakfast: _____
Lunch: _____
Dinner: _____
Snacks: _____

PHYSICAL ACTIVITY steps/miles/minutes: _____
description: _____

SPIRITUAL ACTIVITY
description: _____

LIVE IT TRACKER

Name: _____   Date: _____ Week #: _____

My activity goal for next week:

○ None   ○ <30 min/day   ○ 30-60 min/day

My food goal for next week: _____

_____

loss /gain _____ Calorie Range: _____

My week at a glance:

○ Great   ○ So-so   ○ Not so great

Activity level:

○ None   ○ <30 min/day   ○ 30-60 min/day

RECOMMENDED DAILY AMOUNT OF FOOD FROM EACH GROUP

GROUP	DAILY CALORIES							
....	1300-1400	1500-1600	1700-1800	1900-2000	2100-2200	2300-2400	2500-2600	2700-2800
Fruits	1.5 – 2 c.	1.5 – 2 c.	1.5 – 2 c.	2 – 2.5 c.	2 – 2.5 c.	2.5 – 3.5 c.	3.5 – 4.5 c.	3.5 – 4.5 c.
Vegetables	1.5 – 2 c.	2 – 2.5 c.	2.5 – 3 c.	2.5 – 3 c.	3 – 3.5 c.	3.5 – 4.5 c..	4.5 – 5 c.	4.5 – 5 c.
Grains	5 oz eq.	5-6 oz eq.	6-7 oz eq.	6-7 oz eq.	7-8 oz eq.	8-9 oz eq.	9-10 oz eq.	10-11 oz eq.
Dairy	2-3 c.	3 c.	3 c.	3 c.	3 c.	3 c.	3 c.	3 c.
Protein	4 oz eq.	5 oz eq.	5-5.5 oz eq.	5.5-6.5 oz eq.	6.5-7 oz eq.	7-7.5 oz eq.	7-7.5 oz eq.	7.5-8 oz eq.
Healthy Oils & Other Fats	4 tsp.	5 tsp.	5 tsp.	6 tsp.	6 tsp.	7 tsp.	8 tsp.	8 tsp.
Water & Super Beverages*	Women: 9 c. Men: 13 c.	Women: 9 c. Men: 13 c.	Women: 9 c. Men: 13 c.	Women: 9 c. Men: 13 c.	Women: 9 c. Men: 13 c.	Women: 9 c. Men: 13 c.	Women: 9 c. Men: 13 c.	Women: 9 c. Men: 13 c.

*May count up to 3 cups caffeinated tea or coffee toward goal

DAILY FOOD GROUP TRACKER

GROUP	FRUITS	VEGETABLES	GRAINS	PROTEIN	DAIRY	HEALTHY OILS & OTHER FATS	WATER & SUPER BEVERAGES
❶ Estimate Total							
❷ Estimate Total							
❸ Estimate Total							
❹ Estimate Total							
❺ Estimate Total							
❻ Estimate Total							
❼ Estimate Total							

FOOD CHOICES   DAY ❶

Breakfast: _____

Lunch: _____

Dinner: _____

Snacks: _____

PHYSICAL ACTIVITY   steps/miles/minutes: _____

description: _____

SPIRITUAL ACTIVITY

description: _____

FOOD CHOICES

DAY ②

Breakfast: _____
Lunch: _____
Dinner: _____
Snacks: _____

| PHYSICAL ACTIVITY | steps/miles/minutes: | SPIRITUAL ACTIVITY |

description: _____ | description: _____

FOOD CHOICES

DAY ③

Breakfast: _____
Lunch: _____
Dinner: _____
Snacks: _____

| PHYSICAL ACTIVITY | steps/miles/minutes: | SPIRITUAL ACTIVITY |

description: _____ | description: _____

FOOD CHOICES

DAY ④

Breakfast: _____
Lunch: _____
Dinner: _____
Snacks: _____

| PHYSICAL ACTIVITY | steps/miles/minutes: | SPIRITUAL ACTIVITY |

description: _____ | description: _____

FOOD CHOICES

DAY ⑤

Breakfast: _____
Lunch: _____
Dinner: _____
Snacks: _____

| PHYSICAL ACTIVITY | steps/miles/minutes: | SPIRITUAL ACTIVITY |

description: _____ | description: _____

FOOD CHOICES

DAY ⑥

Breakfast: _____
Lunch: _____
Dinner: _____
Snacks: _____

| PHYSICAL ACTIVITY | steps/miles/minutes: | SPIRITUAL ACTIVITY |

description: _____ | description: _____

FOOD CHOICES

DAY ⑦

Breakfast: _____
Lunch: _____
Dinner: _____
Snacks: _____

| PHYSICAL ACTIVITY | steps/miles/minutes: | SPIRITUAL ACTIVITY |

description: _____ | description: _____

LIVE IT TRACKER

Name: _____

My activity goal for next week:
○ None   ○ <30 min/day   ○ 30-60 min/day

My food goal for next week: _____

Date: _____ Week #: _____

loss /gain _____ Calorie Range: _____

My week at a glance:
○ Great   ○ So-so   ○ Not so great

Activity level:
○ None   ○ <30 min/day   ○ 30-60 min/day

RECOMMENDED DAILY AMOUNT OF FOOD FROM EACH GROUP

GROUP	DAILY CALORIES							
	1300-1400	1500-1600	1700-1800	1900-2000	2100-2200	2300-2400	2500-2600	2700-2800
Fruits	1.5 – 2 c.	1.5 – 2 c.	1.5 – 2 c.	2 – 2.5 c.	2 – 2.5 c.	2.5 – 3.5 c.	3.5 – 4.5 c.	3.5 – 4.5 c.
Vegetables	1.5 – 2 c.	2 – 2.5 c.	2.5 – 3 c.	2.5 – 3 c.	3 – 3.5 c.	3.5 – 4.5 c.	4.5 – 5 c.	4.5 – 5 c.
Grains	5 oz eq.	5-6 oz eq.	6-7 oz eq.	6-7 oz eq.	7-8 oz eq.	8-9 oz eq.	9-10 oz eq.	10-11 oz eq.
Dairy	2-3 c.	3 c.	3 c.	3 c.	3 c.	3 c.	3 c.	3 c.
Protein	4 oz eq.	5 oz eq.	5-5.5 oz eq.	5.5-6.5 oz eq.	6.5-7 oz eq.	7-7.5 oz eq.	7-7.5 oz eq.	7.5-8 oz eq.
Healthy Oils & Other Fats	4 tsp.	5 tsp.	5 tsp.	6 tsp.	6 tsp.	7 tsp.	8 tsp.	8 tsp.
Water & Super Beverages*	Women: 9 c. Men: 13 c.	Women: 9 c. Men: 13 c.	Women: 9 c. Men: 13 c.	Women: 9 c. Men: 13 c.	Women: 9 c. Men: 13 c.	Women: 9 c. Men: 13 c.	Women: 9 c. Men: 13 c.	Women: 9 c. Men: 13 c.

*May count up to 3 cups caffeinated tea or coffee toward goal

DAILY FOOD GROUP TRACKER

GROUP	FRUITS	VEGETABLES	GRAINS	PROTEIN	DAIRY	HEALTHY OILS & OTHER FATS	WATER & SUPER BEVERAGES
❶ Estimate Total							
❷ Estimate Total							
❸ Estimate Total							
❹ Estimate Total							
❺ Estimate Total							
❻ Estimate Total							
❼ Estimate Total							

FOOD CHOICES   DAY ❶

Breakfast: _____
Lunch: _____
Dinner: _____
Snacks: _____

PHYSICAL ACTIVITY   steps/miles/minutes: _____

description: _____

SPIRITUAL ACTIVITY

description: _____

FOOD CHOICES

DAY ❷

Breakfast: _____
Lunch: _____
Dinner: _____
Snacks: _____

PHYSICAL ACTIVITY steps/miles/minutes: _____

SPIRITUAL ACTIVITY

description: _____

description: _____

FOOD CHOICES

DAY ❸

Breakfast: _____
Lunch: _____
Dinner: _____
Snacks: _____

PHYSICAL ACTIVITY steps/miles/minutes: _____

SPIRITUAL ACTIVITY

description: _____

description: _____

FOOD CHOICES

DAY ❹

Breakfast: _____
Lunch: _____
Dinner: _____
Snacks: _____

PHYSICAL ACTIVITY steps/miles/minutes: _____

SPIRITUAL ACTIVITY

description: _____

description: _____

FOOD CHOICES

DAY ❺

Breakfast: _____
Lunch: _____
Dinner: _____
Snacks: _____

PHYSICAL ACTIVITY steps/miles/minutes: _____

SPIRITUAL ACTIVITY

description: _____

description: _____

FOOD CHOICES

DAY ❻

Breakfast: _____
Lunch: _____
Dinner: _____
Snacks: _____

PHYSICAL ACTIVITY steps/miles/minutes: _____

SPIRITUAL ACTIVITY

description: _____

description: _____

FOOD CHOICES

DAY ❼

Breakfast: _____
Lunch: _____
Dinner: _____
Snacks: _____

PHYSICAL ACTIVITY steps/miles/minutes: _____

SPIRITUAL ACTIVITY

description: _____

description: _____

100-MILE CLUB

WALKING			
slowly, 2 mph	30 min =	156 cal =	1 mile
moderately, 3 mph	20 min =	156 cal =	1 mile
very briskly, 4 mph	15 min =	156 cal =	1 mile
speed walking	10 min =	156 cal =	1 mile
up stairs	13 min =	159 cal =	1 mile
RUNNING / JOGGING			
• • •	10 min =	156 cal =	1 mile
CYCLE OUTDOORS			
slowly, < 10 mph	20 min =	156 cal =	1 mile
light effort, 10-12 mph	12 min =	156 cal =	1 mile
moderate effort, 12-14 mph	10 min =	156 cal =	1 mile
vigorous effort, 14-16 mph	7.5 min =	156 cal =	1 mile
very fast, 16-19 mph	6.5 min =	152 cal =	1 mile
SPORTS ACTIVITIES			
playing tennis (singles)	10 min =	156 cal =	1 mile
swimming			
light to moderate effort	11 min =	152 cal =	1 mile
fast, vigorous effort	7.5 min =	156 cal =	1 mile
softball	15 min =	156 cal =	1 mile
golf	20 min =	156 cal =	1 mile
rollerblading	6.5 min =	152 cal =	1 mile
ice skating	11 min =	152 cal =	1 mile
jumping rope	7.5 min =	156 cal =	1 mile
basketball	12 min =	156 cal =	1 mile
soccer (casual)	15 min =	159 min =	1 mile
AROUND THE HOUSE			
mowing grass	22 min =	156 cal =	1 mile
mopping, sweeping, vacuuming	19.5 min =	155 cal =	1 mile
cooking	40 min =	160 cal =	1 mile
gardening	19 min =	156 cal =	1 mile
housework (general)	35 min =	156 cal =	1 mile

AROUND THE HOUSE			
ironing	45 min =	153 cal =	1 mile
raking leaves	25 min =	150 cal =	1 mile
washing car	23 min =	156 cal =	1 mile
washing dishes	45 min =	153 cal =	1 mile
AT THE GYM			
stair machine	8.5 min =	155 cal =	1 mile
stationary bike			
slowly, 10 mph	30 min =	156 cal =	1 mile
moderately, 10-13 mph	15 min =	156 cal =	1 mile
vigorously, 13-16 mph	7.5 min =	156 cal =	1 mile
briskly, 16-19 mph	6.5 min =	156 cal =	1 mile
elliptical trainer	12 min =	156 cal =	1 mile
weight machines (vigorously)	13 min =	152 cal =	1 mile
aerobics			
low impact	15 min =	156 cal =	1 mile
high impact	12 min =	156 cal =	1 mile
water	20 min =	156 cal =	1 mile
pilates	15 min =	156 cal =	1 mile
raquetball (casual)	15 min =	156 cal =	1 mile
stretching exercises	25 min =	150 cal =	1 mile
weight lifting (also works for weight machines used moderately or gently)	30 min =	156 cal =	1 mile
FAMILY LEISURE			
playing piano	37 min =	155 cal =	1 mile
jumping rope	10 min =	152 cal =	1 mile
skating (moderate)	20 min =	152 cal =	1 mile
swimming			
moderate	17 min =	156 cal =	1 mile
vigorous	10 min =	148 cal =	1 mile
table tennis	25 min =	150 cal =	1 mile
walk / run / play with kids	25 min =	150 cal =	1 mile

Let's Count Our Miles!

Color each circle to represent a mile you've completed.
Watch your progress to that 100 mile marker!

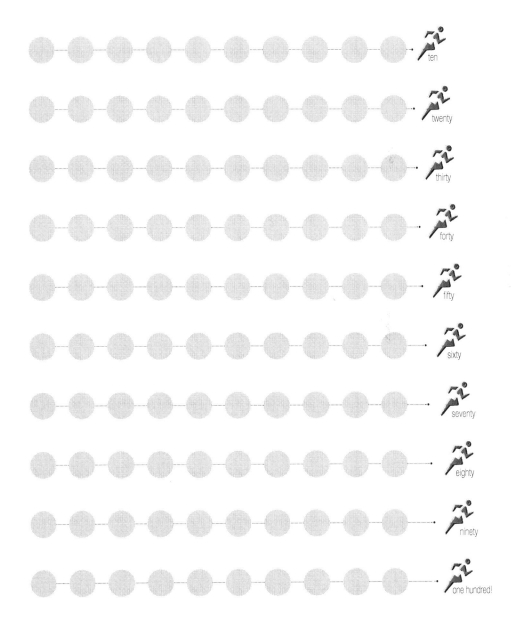

Made in the USA
Columbia, SC
22 July 2022

63851189R00113